31085   QH
541
Engel   E513

Life around us

LIFE AROUND US

Life Around Us

FRITZ-MARTIN ENGEL

Translated from the German by
J. R. FOSTER

THOMAS Y. CROWELL COMPANY
New York · Established 1834

First published in the United States of America in 1965

Originally published in German under the
title ZWISCHEN NULL UND FUENF

German edition copyright © 1961 Bayerischer
Landwirtschaftsverlag GmbH.

English translation copyright © 1965
by GEORGE G. HARRAP & CO. LTD
and THOMAS Y. CROWELL COMPANY

Printed in Great Britain

Library of Congress Catalog Card No. 65-13816

Contents

Plates

Introduction

Overworked phrases like 'the struggle for existence', 'the fight for living space', 'the search for food, light, and warmth', 'peaceful co-existence', 'the instinct for self-preservation', are only clichés used to describe what biologists mean by 'ecological harmony', the balanced adaptation, which is the basic principle of living together. At the same time, the need for equilibrium also dictates the relative values of all the other biological laws—those concerned with feeding, the elimination of waste, growth, reproduction, and death. In all the varied manifestations of Nature, every single form of life—the weak and the strong, the long-suffering and the impatient, the gregarious and those who travel alone—has its own part to play in the scheme as a whole, and contributes to the continuation of the complex of living things. The beauty and power so obvious in the largest and apparently most perfect plants and animals are of no more significance than the beauty and perfection which the microscope can find in a crumb of earth. Everything in nature forms part of a whole whose wonders extend to the very limit of our ability to perceive them, and which may properly be described as endless.

Let us therefore study all the creatures of the earth's crust. Living things, in almost infinite variety, are adapted to ways of life as diverse as those of the insignificant amoeba in a gutter, the reptile, the bacillus living in a sick organism, the fish, the algae in the soil, the bird, and finally man—the apex of the process of evolution. But man's ideas about the world—which have their roots in dreams, superstition, myths, fear, and magic and in the longing for knowledge, truth, and deliverance—have in our day been profoundly transformed by the advance of learning and research. We can see smaller and smaller things with the electron microscope; objects farther and farther away can be traced by radar; special cameras can take 200,000 different photographs in a second; satellites can take a single photograph of half the world; distances of less than one thousandth of a millimetre can be gauged; and chronometers can be made which vary hardly a second in decades and measure time to within thousandths of a second. *Homo sapiens* of the twentieth century has some of his thinking done for him by electronic computers, which are capable of adding 5000 ten-figure numbers in the space of a split second.

In an age of such astounding successes and almost daily sensations, man is almost in danger of forgetting to keep his feet on the ground, literally as well as figuratively! The ground beneath our feet determines the fundamental character of the landscape; some of its features are strongly marked, but even these are in a state of perpetual change, like everything else on the surface of the earth. The soil, which eventually provides us with our food, is itself the result of an involved set of processes. Fertile soil is not a dead substance made up of inorganic minerals, but a complex of organisms, and the ground is a home for every living organism that grows, puts forth leaves and blossoms, that flies, runs or crawls.

I Growth and Change

THE EARTH'S CRUST

The earth's restless crust was formed by the gradual cooling of molten matter. In its early days the earth was hot, barren, and empty; but, by a process that lasted for thousands of years, the face of our planet was gradually sculptured out of this mass of molten lava. The interplay of the two great geological forces, diastrophism and denudation, gave the continents their present shape. The land surface of our planet is continually and slowly changing; it may seem to us fixed and unchanged for all eternity, but it is in fact in continual movement, although major changes only become apparent after millions of years. Periods of mountain building alternate with periods of denudation and levelling out. Mountain chains such as the Alps, Himalayas, Caucasus, Andes, and Cordilleras were forced up from the earth's crust in folds; once they were regarded as 'the backbones of the continents', yet, in fact, they are only wrinkles in the crust of the earth, insignificant in relation to the whole.

Icy glaciers, frost and heat, storm and rain, running waters, and rushing winds all play their part in eroding these wrinkles. Living organisms, too, are ceaselessly at work splitting, sawing, gnawing, and loosening the land surface stone by stone, grain by grain. In the long run these tiny, slow, but continuous processes do more to change the landscape than the great natural catastrophes which occur periodically.

Water, a beautiful and terrifying element, the supporter of life, also possesses incalculable destructive power. In the deforested clay of Georgia, small clefts have grown in twenty years into ravines over fifty feet deep; in the scree-slopes of Vesuvius, gullies twenty feet deep have been hollowed out in less than three days; and a mountain stream in Switzerland, the much-feared Nolla, once furrowed its bed over ninety feet deeper in less than forty-eight hours. These are exceptional cases, of course; usually, effective erosion by water takes many thousands of years; and it took water's sawing action a million years to make the Colorado Canyon what it is today.

Wind, too, helps to erode the landscape, especially in places where the ground has dried out and few plants grow. It works like a sand-blaster, laying bare the rocky subsoil, cutting out grooves, furrows, and honeycombs, or chiselling curious mushroom-like cliffs, towers, and tables. The eroding action of wind varies considerably according to the structure of the ground and according to the arrangement, size, and powers of resistance of the rock. The surface of dense or fine-grained stone generally becomes pitted with small holes, while the coarser substances develop hollows of various kinds: holes, grooves, structures like mushrooms, lattice work, pans, and kettles. The swift and total pulverization of rock by the wind, a process particularly characteristic of sun-drenched, salty wildernesses, produces the finest material from joints and cracks and corners.

The great stabilizers of erosion are plants. They protect the surface of the ground, break the force of the wind, and keep the ground moist, strengthening it with their roots.

Besides water and wind, there is also ice, which is comparable in its erosive action to a plane. Huge as some alpine glaciers may seem to be today, they are tiny in comparison with the great sheets and rivers of ice of prehistoric times. Extending over millions of square miles, and hundreds of feet thick, the glaciers of the Ice Ages rubbed old mountain ranges smooth and left in their wake lines of moraine as high as hills. When they melted, water soon filled the innumerable inland lakes dammed by moraines and created huge river valleys.

The forces that raise the earth's crust and those that wear it away tend to balance each other; there is still plenty of activity going on below the mantle of our restless earth, as earthquakes and volcanoes bear witness. For aeons, the continents have been rising slowly and falling, experiencing folds and thrusts produced by enormous alterations in pressure and the natural striving in the earth's crust to create an equilibrium between the regions with 'bulges' and those with 'depressions'.

As well as these large-scale changes in the form of the earth's crust there is the organic chemical transformation of the ground by the

12

acidity resulting from the decay of organic substances, particularly plants. Although living, rooted plants protect the ground against erosion by wind and water, they also have a destructive effect on it: their roots force their way into crevices and split even the hardest rock as they grow, thus creating new material for water and the atmosphere to carry away. The split and corroded rock provides a foothold for a fresh succession of plants. Starting with bacteria, algae, and fungi, this process of 'biological weathering', which affects hard rocks like granite and basalt just as much as porous chalk, eventually opens the way to more highly developed plants: lichens and mosses, ferns, grass, bushes, and trees. Finally, the activity of all kinds of digging and burrowing animals can also affect the structure and rigidity of the ground.

All these influences together determine the appearance of the earth's surface, in the primitive forest and on the steppe, on boulder-strewn mountains, in the arctic tundra, and the fertile meadows and fields of the temperate zones.

EARLIEST FORMS OF LIFE

Life presumably began in the sea with insignificant single-celled forms, undifferentiated lumps of protoplasm, which can be compared with the simplest algae. It was an unimaginably long time before the land, too, could be inhabited by these primitive forms of life. Another enormous period of time had to pass before the earliest multi-celled forms developed out of the lowest organisms. However, we do know that the very first gemmiparous or budding plants appear as inhabitants of dry land in the Lower Devonian formation, some 300 million years ago. Thanks to exceptionally favourable conditions for fossilization, the structure of many of these early plant inhabitants of the earth is almost as well known as that of present-day plants. Over 300 million years ago lycopodiums, lepidodendrons, and tree-like horsetails formed zones of vegetation over wide areas of the earth. The luxuriant spread of vegetation was the precondition for the conquest of the land by animal life as well. The seas already harboured animal forms of every category, from single-celled protozoa and other primitive animals up to fish, the first vertebrates. The first lung-fish started to survive dry periods in the mud of shallow coasts and creeks, and eventually their swim-bladders evolved into lungs and their fins into limbs, so that they could move about on dry land. By the Carboniferous period, this process of transition from fish to amphibian was long complete.

13

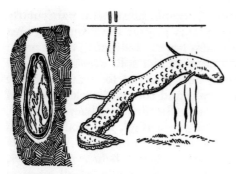

The African lung-fish has a lung as well as gills. The lung has developed from the swim-bladder. During the dry season, the lung-fish digs a hole in the mud and encases itself in slime, which turns hard.

Flying reptiles flapped across the sky; through the twilight of the glistening, swampy forests, with their narrow-leafed trees and forty-foot-high lepidodendrons, hummed the first insects, among them the giant dragonfly *Meganeura* with a wing span of nearly a yard; and over the fern fronds crept huge cockroaches, and fantastic bugs, scorpions, and spiders. The vegetation grew richer and richer in form and kind, until at last in the Tertiary, some 50 million years ago, the blossoming plants developed in unimaginable variety.

Today the number of different forms in the plant world is almost incalculable, yet it is only a section of the organic development which has taken place during the course of the earth's history and indeed is still going on.

The identification and classification of fossilized plants is often extremely difficult because, owing to their size, most plants were torn to pieces before being embedded, so that we possess only fragments of them. The further back we go in the rock formations, the more the fossil plant remains differ from living plants of today and the more uncertain our ecological conclusions become. Paleobotany, the study of fossil plants, must, therefore, always work hand in hand with geology, for it is necessary to interpret the environment and where possible to investigate the layer in which the vegetation was once rooted.

The likelihood of preservation is greatest in those cases where the plant itself builds up a framework out of some mineral. We have only to think of the diatoms with their silica skeletons. Diatoms have existed for millions of years and countless generations. The fossil forms of the Carboniferous period, to which huge deposits of diatomaceous earth in many different places bear eloquent witness, resemble very closely forms still living, even in the particular characteristics of different species. In addition, diatomaceous earth contains rich

14

remains of water and land plants and also remains of water and land animals.

Of course, it is extremely rare for plants to secrete a mineral framework; the phenomenon is confined almost entirely to a few species of algae. So far as the remains of most other prehistoric plants are concerned, the organic substance may be either completely or partly preserved; or it may have disappeared and left only an impression behind; or again it may have been completely replaced by a mineral such as silica or calcite.

In the case of carbonization, the vegetable matter, deprived of oxygen, turns first into peat, then into brown coal, and finally into hard coal. In Tertiary deposits and Quaternary bogs, remains with good powers of resistance such as seeds, fruit, and grains of pollen are often so well preserved that we can easily determine their texture under the microscope. If decay goes further in rock containing the remains of plants, only a hollow or a structureless impression is left in their place.

To assess the living conditions of prehistoric plants it is of the greatest importance to know whether they lived in the spot where they were found in the rock or whether they have been carried there by rivers from another, perhaps far-distant, place before becoming embedded. Ocean currents, in particular, sometimes carried the more resistant parts of plants, such as fruit and sticks, considerable distances before they sank to be preserved in the sediment.

For a long time people did not understand how to interpret animal fossils and regarded them as curious freaks of nature or as mysterious objects endowed with magic powers and originating in the activity of supernatural creatures. In the last two centuries knowledge of their true nature has become more and more widespread, and we also know more or less how these relics of prehistoric animals have been preserved. We know that when an animal dies events usually occur which quickly lead to decomposition and destruction of the corpse, events determined by chemical and biological factors (temperature, humidity, bacteria, and carrion-eating animals) aided by mechanical and climatic factors (dispersal, wetting, drying, etc.). Only swift covering may in some cases halt decay. It must have been the same in prehistoric times. Covering by sediment is the precondition for the creation of a fossil; at least it puts a stop to the process of aerobic decay. Pressure increased with the superposition of further masses of sediment or layers of rock and was capable of increasing the changes of fossilization.

Brontops, *a 13-foot herbivorous monster of the Eocene period. Reconstruction was from fossilized remains, which indicate that it belonged to the unequalhoofed animals. (Based on Osborn, with alterations.)*

Big changes in the animal world seem to have been linked with big changes in the plant world—transformations of the fauna were preceded by transformations of the flora; new kinds of plants provided the nourishment for new kinds of animals. For example, we cannot fail to recognize the connection between the development of the hoofed animals that live in herds and the change from forest to grassland that took place in the Tertiary Era. The appearance of the blossom-visiting insects in the Jurassic and Cretaceous periods is linked up with the development of blossoming plants.

Paleobiology is founded on the recognition of the relations that exist between each living thing and its environment, and between adaptation and function, in order to meet the manifold demands of existence. These demands differ according to habitat and manner of life—for example, the reindeer in the arctic tundra lives differently from the giraffe in the African scrub or the chamois in the Alps. Again, the reindeer lives differently from the musk-ox or the lemming, and the chamois lives differently from the mountain goat or the alpine hare.

Not only do these various animals live differently, their bodies are also differently constructed. Adaptation to environment demands the development of particular patterns of behaviour and physical shapes. With mammals, this is most obvious in the formation of the limbs and teeth. Remains of teeth and bones are therefore particularly informative for the paleozoologist, which is fortunate because they are usually the only parts to be preserved. Not only do they indicate whether the limbs were slender or plump, but also whether they ended in hoof or claws.

The tracks of prehistoric animals are no less informative. They are more perishable, but in certain favourable circumstances, if they were made in fine sediment that soon hardened and were covered up quickly by sediment, they are well preserved. These footprints tell us a great deal—for example, the way in which the animals moved can often be deduced with astonishing certainty. We can see whether the animal ran, climbed, crawled, or burrowed in the earth. Even the speed of movement can be assessed, for it is possible to tell whether the tread was light or heavy and whether the animal was a runner, a jumper, or a trotter. From a well-preserved track, the paleozoologist can estimate the length of the stride, the respective size of the fore and hind limbs, and the approximate size of the animal's body.

Very often fossilized remains will tell us whether the animal was at home in the marshy forest or on a rocky terrain, whether it lived on grassy steppes or in an arctic wilderness, and whether the ground was rich in organic matter, and so on.

Still clearer indications about an animal's diet and mode of life, and about the animals and plants of its environment, are provided by the form and wear of the jaws and above all by the remains of food which have occasionally been preserved between the teeth or in the skeleton of the carcass (stones, pellets, fossilized excrement, among other things).

Other traces of life that have been found inform us about growth and reproduction. They tell us of the mutual relations between the members of living communities, of struggles for living room and food, or of forms of symbiosis, parasitism, commensalism, and so forth. Furthermore, we learn of the accidents suffered by animals and above all of many kinds of disease. In prehistoric land vertebrates we find traces of abnormalities and malformations, as well as of diseases of the teeth and jaw; broken bones; inflammation of the muscles, periosteum, bone marrow, and joints; rickets; and tuberculosis of the joints. The position of the fossils in the earth and the situation of their separate parts in relation to each other also give indications of the manner of death. Insects preserved in amber from the early Tertiary era quite often give us a direct insight into the circumstances of death; for example, insects and spiders exhibit torn-out legs, traces of dragging and scratching; and other details which provide evidence of vain attempts to regain freedom.

Life unfolded during the course of long epochs. Its beginnings are lost in complete obscurity. Later series of developments and forms of life have become known to us as fossils, thanks to fortuitously good conditions for preservation. Thus we learn that the history of the species, genera, and families reflects differing tempos of transformation. Often a swift upsurge in evolutionary development was followed by a period of stability and finally by a decline to the point of extinction.

Let us look first at insects. Their distribution on dry land is almost unlimited, for they use many different kinds of things for food and adapt themselves to an equally wide range of environments. It is in the tropics, where the stream of life on land is in general broader and swifter than elsewhere, that they display their most luxuriant and bizarre forms and an extravagant abundance of species. But even in the regions where life is less abundant they manage to hold out, often in the hardest conditions imaginable. There are land insects even in the arctic and antarctic wastes, where the only plants are a few poor lichens struggling for existence on the otherwise naked rock; other insects live in the hottest deserts, where the scorching sun scarcely permits life.

There are insects which live in the muddy floors of the deepest caves, where the sun never penetrates, and others which live on storm-girt islands in the ocean and on the glaciers of mountains. In view of the great variation in environment it is not surprising that the structure and habits of insects display an amazing multiplicity, which is reflected in the numerous families, genera, and species into which they are divided. Moreover, the rôle of the land insects is intertwined so closely with the rest of the living natural cycle that their disappearance would completely transform the whole of life on earth.

The origin and early development of the land insects is lost in the mists of time. This is partly because the early insects were small and extremely fragile, and therefore disappeared without leaving behind any remains that could be preserved as fossils, and partly because the rock sediments from those days have been fundamentally altered by processes of pressure and earth movement, and sometimes of heat, over millions of years. The first fossils that can be identified with certainty as those of winged insects date from the Carboniferous period of some 250 million years ago. The huge forests of lepidodendrons, tree ferns, and similar plants offered an abundance of food. The first vertebrates—amphibians, and primitive reptiles—had by this time already taken their first steps on dry land. Most of the insects which lived in the Carboniferous period have disappeared today. Among the few that have survived are the cockroaches. The insects that have come down to us from the succeeding millennia show more and more resemblance to those of the present day. A large number are known from Tertiary amber, which is about 30 million years old. The condition of insects such as flies and ants imprisoned in this fossilized resin is so good that the finest details of their physical structure can be made out.

Among the oldest land animals are the arachnids, which are known to have existed in the Devonian and Carboniferous periods. They have come off well in the ecological struggle with the insects that appeared about the same time; there are, for example, the scorpions and the 20,000 species of web-spinning spiders. It is in fact the smallest of them—the mites, most of them between a tenth of a millimetre and two millimetres long—that can claim to be the most widely

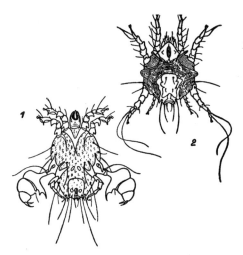

Parasitic Mites
   1. Analges chelopus, *a mite that lives as a parasite on small birds. Note the third pair of legs, which have been transformed into huge organs for clinging.*
   2. Otodectes sp., *a parasite that lives in the outer ear passages of cats. It causes purulent inflammation of the ear.*

distributed. They have conquered every inch of dry land, and some even live a considerable distance underground. There are mites all over the world, in every climate and in every zoographical region. Many are free-living and feed on dead organic matter; others prey on smaller insects, or live on and in plants, sucking their sap or devouring their cells; and yet others live as parasites on higher animals. The most harmless of these are the species which dwell as external parasites on beetles, flies, and other small insects, or are to be found as 'messmates' in the nests of ants, bees, and wasps and in the underground tunnels of bark beetles. Many mites live on birds and mammals, feeding on the gland secretions, skin, feathers, or hair of their hosts, or else sucking their blood. More burdensome, and indeed sometimes extremely dangerous, are the species which cause skin diseases such as mange in beasts of prey and hoofed

19

animals (dogs, foxes, chamois, ibexes) or the so-called 'itch' in human beings.

The harmless-looking horned mites live in the earth, in moss, in decaying foliage, and in the rotten wood of fallen tree trunks, feeding on humus, algae, fungi, and the droppings of many animals. Until recently they seemed to possess no ecological significance beyond that of turning over the humus, but modern, mainly American, research has shown that many of them act as temporary hosts for the tapeworm—which is a serious animal parasite. Apart from such special cases, however, the land mites have a positive biological importance, for the great majority of them, as a result of their manner of feeding, are 'active' soil organisms and play a direct part in the soil processes. In density they far exceed all other arthropods living in the ground. This density gives them a notable share in the work of the organisms in the soil environment; they help to loosen and aerate the soil, to break up vegetable waste, and to effect its chemical transformation into humus. Their contribution is all the more valuable because the decomposition of tissue in the mite's intestine goes a long way and cellulose is scarcely ever left intact.

We know for certain that the birds are descended from the reptiles, although not from species still extant. The arrangement of the arteries, the scales on the feet, and the structure of the skull show the relationship of birds to scaly reptiles. It has long been disputed whether the primitive bird *Archaeopteryx*, which lived 150 million years ago, and was preserved in the lithographic stone in the Jurassic strata of Eichstadt, was still a lizard or already a bird. Its foot is certainly like that of a bird and it had feathers, but its teeth, eyes, and 23 vertebrae are reptilian. It was probably in the Triassic period that the ancestors of the birds began to part company with the reptiles and to conquer the air.

For at least 75 million years, in the geological Middle Ages, the saurians ruled the scene on land and in the sea; many were herbivorous, but some were beasts of prey. Many of the land forms walked or hopped on two legs; others remained four-footed. Some of the latter were as fleet as antelopes, others as ponderous as elephants. Many were grotesque giants, so heavy that they could only live half submerged in marshes, where the water helped to support the weight of their bodies. They were not adapted to changing conditions and so died out; the land became too dry and food became scarce.

Then the great age of mammals arrived. When we come to study the mammals, in whatever direction we look we always find an inner harmony between physical structure, environment, and mode of life. For example, we only have to consider the differing manner of contact with the ground: some mammals walk on the soles of their feet (bear, badger), others on the toes (cat, dog), and others on the tips of the toes (ox, horse). The limbs of mammals also show

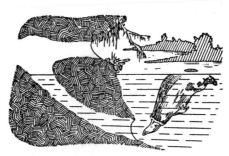

The duck-billed platypus of Australia has a flattened beak like the duck, lays eggs like a bird, suckles its young through pores in its belly as it has no teats, burrows like a mole, and swims in water like a beaver.

extreme variety in length and strength, in the way they are set in the body, the way they are equipped with nails, claws, or hoofs, and various other details. The climbers and the beasts of prey developed paws and claws; the swift runners turned the claw into a hoof.

Let us take as an example the evolution of the rhinoceros, a story which is better known than that of many other families of animals. We know that the rhinoceroses evolved at the beginning of the Tertiary era from small, dainty, hornless animals which lived in the bush and were related to the ancestors of the horse and the tapir. All these original species had five toes on each foot. The tapirs remained forest-dwellers; today they have four toes on the forefoot and three on the hindfoot, and are thus protected against the danger of sinking into the wet banks of rivers. Horses became swift steppe-dwellers; each of their feet bears only one toe, which is particularly strong and powerful. Rhinoceroses, however, have three toes on each foot forming broad supporting surfaces for the enormous weight of their ponderous bodies.

On the other hand, in the case of the animals with an even number of toes the pressure of the body falls between toes three and four, which share the burden between them and therefore become equally strong. As a result of their unified function, these toes, or if not the toes then the metatarsal and metacarpal bones next to them, coalesce. The main representatives of this group are the animals that man

21

either keeps or hunts: oxen, buffaloes, sheep, goats, antelope, camels and llamas, stags, giraffes, and pigs.

The teeth give a reliable indication whether a mammal is carnivorous, herbivorous, or omnivorous. For example, the discovery of one single fossilized molar enables a skilled investigator to form a fundamentally accurate picture of the animal in question and to place the animal with a high degree of probability at the right place in the story of evolution. Insect-eaters and numerous rodents that use the forelimbs for snatching, climbing, or burrowing have shoulder blades and well-developed collar bones like men, but mammals which in running only move their forelegs backwards and forwards, or just use them as supports in jumping, either have no collar bones at all or only rudimentary ones.

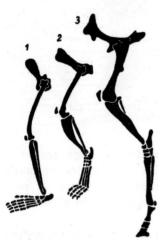

The gait of mammals: 1. Plantigrade; 2. Digitigrade; 3. Unguligrade.

A decisive step on the path to man was the transition to an upright position. The upright walk, the development of the hands, the higher specialization of the brain, the training of the voice for speech as a means of expressing thought, all represent a consistent process of evolution. Apart from these advantages, his upright position has brought man the considerable disadvantage of slowing down his means of locomotion. There is no other vertebrate of similar size which is so uncertain in its progress and executes its natural walk so badly as man. But all the defects of our body and senses are outweighed by the acquisition of a creative hand and a thinking, inventive brain.

Many series of mammals began with small, nimble forms and ended with big, clumsy forms. This 'tendency to increase in size' is valid not only in the case of the saurians but also in the case of elephants, giant armadillos, rhinoceroses, and so on, whose earliest ancestors were mammals of very much smaller size. The greater the size of the animal, the longer it takes to reach sexual maturity and the smaller the number of young produced by each individual—the elephant bears young about once every eight years—which also means a diminished chance of survival in the struggle to exist. The small animals with high rates of reproduction—for example, the fieldmouse, which produces four to ten offspring every two months— have a far better prospect of surviving natural catastrophes or marked deterioration of living conditions; here numbers are victorious.

In absolute numbers the most abundant living creatures are 'micro-organisms', usually with only one cell, and the old saying that Nature is at her greatest in the smallest things is also true in the sense that the insignificant in size is quite often the most important. The 'primitive' single-celled creatures are highly specialized and all the vital functions are compressed in one single drop of protoplasm; indeed, the pioneers of microbiology, sitting at their ornate

Trichopteryx atomaria, *the smallest beetle in the world, widely distributed in decaying vegetable matter, under moss and stones, in roots, and also in ants' nests. Size, about* 15 *millimetres.*

'flea-glasses', had serious doubts whether they were single cells and regarded them as 'animalcula'—miniature animals with eyes, bowels, bones, and even a brain. If today, in spite of all the knowledge we have gained, we cling to the notion of the 'simplicity' of these organisms, that is only because we have a fundamentally wider conception of the 'single cell'. Some algae and protozoa build themselves outer protective covers; they contain inner frameworks of perfect symmetry; they have cavities, swallowing mechanisms, organs of secretion, and unimaginably minute muscle fibres. With protoplasmic feet, with outer and inner streams of protoplasm, with flagella and cilia, they swim, steer, and feel their way forwards in the ground and in water. All this, in all its unsuspected abundance and capacity for modification, is a mysterious, hidden world, which provides us, via the smallest unicellular being, with a key to the most fundamental questions of organic life, to the manifold phenomena of form and function, reproduction and evolution, adaptation and protection, symbiosis and parasitism, and all the other privileges which distinguish the living organism from the dead matter of the inorganic world.

23

Take bacteria: however guilty some may be of causing illness and disease in men and animals, the resulting suffering and inconvenience are only a small price to pay for the work which other forms carry out for us. Nowhere does one realize more clearly how mistaken it is to regard bacteria as purely harmful than when one examines their rôle in the soil processes. They assist in the preparation of mineral and organic components and contribute to the preservation of the fertility of the soil. At the same time some species of bacteria play

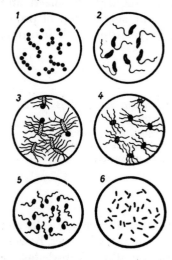

The Activities of Bacteria
1. Streptococcus pyogenes, *the cause of blood-poisoning and numerous inflammations.*
2. Vibrio cholerae, *the cholera germ.*
3. Bacillus tetani, *the lockjaw bacillus with spores.*
4. Bacillus radicicola, *which causes the enrichment of nitrogen in the root nodules of the Leguminosae.*
5. Nitrosomonas *converts the ammonia compounds in arable land into nitrite.*
6. Nitrobacter *is instrumental in trans-forming the nitrites in the ground into nitrates.*

an important part in the nourishment of higher plants by fixing atmospheric nitrogen, which is not directly available to higher plants. As a result of this activity on the part of bacteria, nitrogen is in continuous circulation between air, soil organisms, the soil, and green plants. Nitrogen passes from the air into the ground via the nitrogen-fixing bacteria of the soil and via lightning flashes. Where these nitrogen-fixing bacteria live in a symbiotic association with plants, the nitrogen passes directly into the plants; from the plants, it passes into the herbivorous animals and some of it then becomes part of carnivorous animals. From the last two it returns to the earth via excreta and corpses.

The strangely cleft mountain landscape bears witness to the interplay of powerful natural forces (Ago di Sciora in Bergell). (Photo: W. Flaig.)

(Overleaf) The glacier has dug its bed through the rocks like a chisel through a piece of wood. The aerial photograph makes it particularly easy to pick out the lateral moraines—the line of débris along the sides of the glacier. (Photo: Bradford/Washburn/Bavaria.)

These curiously shaped cliffs, towers, and gorges have been worn out of the rock by the force of flowing water (a canyon at an altitude of 7800 feet in the Yellowstone National Park, U. S. A.) (Photo: Dr Wolff und Trischler.)

2 *Structure of the Ground*

HELP OR HINDRANCE TO LIFE

The various land regions which support life differ widely; they range from wide regions, natural and cultural, to minute, often temporary scenes of activity. The moulding of the large-scale regions is determined largely by climate, which produces landscapes whose mere physical appearance is in itself striking: tundras, equatorial and monsoon forests, steppes, deserts, and so on. These so-called 'bioregions' embrace in turn numerous 'habitats', which provide, as a result of particular historical, pedological or climatic causes, or of other natural processes (and, not least, of the activity of man) sharply differentiated living conditions within short distances of each other. Examples of such habitats or 'biotopes' are dunes, fields, meadows, moors, woods, marshes, rock slopes, and so on.

These regions are interwoven on both a large and a small scale with transitional, border areas, which combine the conditions of the various regions in a sort of mosaic. Examples of large-scale transitional areas are the wooded steppes of south Russia, where the animals of the forest and the open steppe-land mingle, and the huge poplar woods between the taiga and the steppe in Canada. In such cases the flora and fauna conform to environmental factors in varying degrees, and just the same thing happens on a smaller scale in the border and fringe biocœnoses[1]; for example, on the edges of forests, on the banks of rivers, on the snowline in the mountains, and on the margins of glaciers. It is not surprising that the different elements in these adjacent habitats quite often create extremely favourable and varied conditions of life. For example, hedges and

[1] A biocœnosis is a community of individuals of different species. (Translator.)

31085

the verges of forests offer enough light for sun-loving species, but they also provide welcome shade for nocturnal animals and ideal refuges, hiding places, and hibernating conditions for small animals of every kind. Again, every layer of soil, every centre of activity, contains areas with communities of particularly characteristic forms, which are usually almost independent of each other. This is true of the roots of plants, of the bark of a tree trunk, and, when we come to the ground itself, of its immediate surface, the decaying vegetation on top, the firm structure underneath and also the air- and water-filled spaces between the soil particles.

The communities of plants and animals found on dry land can be properly understood only if we are familiar with the conditions of life—that is, the peculiarities of individual environments.

The soil of our planet, both on the surface and below it, is characterized, so far as environmental conditions are concerned, by favourable and unfavourable spots. There are regions where the conditions of life are favourable for a particularly large number of organisms, places where the environmental factors are exceptionally harmonious and well balanced; in these places life can achieve its optimum development. Optimum development means simply the greatest abundance of species, living in ecological balance, with the greatest possible productive dynamism, and the widest use of all the living space available. On the other hand, there are places where the chemical, physical, and ecological conditions are so favourable to a few species that these attain an extreme development; this means impoverishment of the communities of organisms, and the species embracing large numbers of individuals, usually with a markedly similar character, are strongly adapted to the environment.

Thus it is worth emphasizing again that the characteristics of the soil structures, the temperature, the conditions of light and air, and not least the facilities for feeding, breeding, and finding protection, can all become either helps or hindrances to life. What is particularly striking is the fact that it is the mechanical properties of the soil—the coarseness or fineness of its structure—that help to give the face of the inhabited earth its outward appearance and influence in a multitude of ways the development, activity, and selection of plant and animal life.

PLANTS ROOTED IN THE SOIL

The distribution over the earth's surface of most of the plant life that occurs in nature is by no means irregular or fortuitous. On the contrary, the layer of vegetation which covers the earth and determines the appearance of the landscape reflects fairly strict divisions caused by the tendency of certain communities of plants to unified grouping. However, of all the factors which affect land vegetation the most important is water, the abundance and availability of which is again influenced by the structure of the soil.

Sandy soil retains substantially less water after rain than soil rich in clay or humus, which is capable of feeding springs but on the other hand ties up a larger percentage of the water in a way that makes it unavailable to plants. On the whole, the absorptive power of normal cultivated soil is fairly small; in this respect normal soil is quite unlike typical saline or desert soil. The root hairs, with their capacity for osmotic absorption, always have to overcome considerable resistance in their task of extracting water from the ground, for the soil particles hold on to it stubbornly; it is therefore not surprising that the osmotic capacities of plants vary tremendously according to site and species. In the bean, it is two to three and a half atmospheres; in the nasturtium it is about five atmospheres; in mangrove plants up to twenty; and in desert plants it goes up to one hundred atmospheres.

The great importance to vegetation of the soil structure can best be appreciated from the example of extreme situations like deserts and the polar regions.

Deserts account for almost a fifth of the land surface of the globe. There are all kinds of deserts—sand, rock, clay and salt deserts; high plateaux and low-lying wadis—and each of them has its own ecological character and a vegetation adapted to the structure of its soil. On the whole, in desert regions plants play only a small part in covering the ground, and this is due to the exceptional difficulty of finding enough water. As desert storms are usually confined to a limited area, the average rainfall of a whole desert is insignificant. When the rain does arrive, it comes down in short, usually violent cloudbursts; as a result, the water soon runs away over the bare and generally hardened ground as though over a piece of asphalt. A few hours later the only visible reminder of the downpour is a number of damp, muddy spots which soon grow dry and stiff under the burning rays of the sun.

However, desert plants can exist even in these extreme conditions. For example, the annual 'rain plants' spend most of the year with their seeds quietly resting on or in the ground; after the first rain they spring up out of the ground as if by magic. Other desert plants reduce losses through evaporation by discarding all vegetation above ground during the dry season; only the roots remain alive. Some of these plants are succulents, like the various species of cactus in the less extreme North American deserts, but most of them are low bushes, shrubs, and grasses, which grip the sandy soil with their stems, leaves and thorny roots, and by means of their high absorptive capacity and a richly developed root system draw nutrient salts and what water there is from a wide area of ground, subsequently storing up their gains for many months. Usually the roots do not go very deep, but spread out at a depth of only three to six feet below the surface. On the other hand, some roots are long, and go on growing downward until they reach strata that hold sufficient water.

Many deserts—large parts of the Sahara, for example—are characterized by wind-blown shifting sand, which, in conjunction with the abrupt changes in temperature, gradually demolishes the rock. Quite often the outside of the rock grows brittle and splits off in big, flat pieces with a noise like a gunshot.

In these regions of drifting sand, grasses and plants with creeping stems play the part of pioneers in the work of consolidating the soil, as they do, for example, in the dunes along the northern coast of Germany. Only after this process can other plants like the thorny acacia and the tamarisk shrub become established. Rock deserts like the northern and central parts of the Sahara, where brownish-black, angular rubble covers wide expanses of ground, are largely hostile to life. Much the same is true of the salt deserts which occur quite frequently in Asia, Australia, and the western part of South America. Much of the ground in these deserts is paved with the salt arising from the weathering of the rocks—it looks like a layer of ice—and the rest is so rich in salt that very few plants are capable of taking root there. Those that do must possess high osmotic absorptiveness, so as to be able to draw water from such compressed, salty soil.

The tundra of the polar regions demonstrates even more impressively than do tropical deserts how important the structure of the soil is in shaping the appearance of the earth's surface, for it is once again the soil that gives the landscape between the Arctic Ocean and the tree line its characteristic stamp. In the arctic wilderness the ground does not thaw deep enough in summer for trees to anchor their roots in it, but it does thaw sufficiently for herbaceous plants and dwarf bushes to grow. The long winter frosts make the ground of the tundra as hard as a rock, and thus cut down erosion by wind and water to very small proportions. However, they do cause changes, if only small ones, in the few inches of ground which thaw every year. Hence the characteristic polygonal structure of arctic ground, with its rings, polygons, banks, and strips, which are emphasized by rows of stones and gullies, and in whose crevices the vegetation takes root. Here the seedlings find valuable humus and also protection from the raw winds.

The origin of these phenomena, which occur in many arctic lands —Greenland and northern Siberia, for example—has been explained in many ways. What is certain is that this kind of soil structure is only possible where the earth is frozen for most of the year and only thaws periodically on the surface. When the ground of the tundra freezes, the fine material—which holds more water— is subject to greater expansion (owing to the freezing of the water in it) than gravel and stones, which for their part are forced outwards in all directions by the resulting pressure. When the ground thaws again, the finer, denser material contracts, but the gravel and stones stay where they are. This process, which is repeated several times every autumn and spring, leads to a regular 'sorting out' of the ground's constituents: the stones are pushed farther and farther out from the centre of the resulting circles and polygons, whose diameter varies from an inch or two to several yards. The dry climate, the short season in which vegetation can grow, and not least the structure of the permanently frozen substratum (permafrost), determine the character of the vegetation to be found in the tundra. The plants are low and squat, and often grow in cushions or clumps, which gives them particularly good protection against the wind. The roots, hampered in their activity by the extreme acidity of the poorly drained, cold soil, spread out not far below the surface of the ground. In this the polar region shows great similarity to the corresponding zone in mountain chains; both are regions beyond the protective roofing of the forest, peopled only by the pioneers of plant life. And in these regions where taller plants cannot thrive we find huge flat patches of brightly coloured lichens, whose modest needs and good resistance to cold and acidity make them ideally suited to the Arctic. In many places they prepare the way for higher plants, which can then gain a foothold in the humus that collects under the beds of lichen.

Desert and tundra will serve as particularly distinctive examples of the many areas where there are close links between the structure of the soil and the vegetation. Other examples are rock and scree slopes, with their loose stones and humus-building pioneer vegetation, the grasses of the savannah, with their highly specialized root systems, and tropical rain forests with the curious root formations of their trees—fantastically shaped supporting roots and stilt roots, the thorny roots of palms, and the mud plants of mangrove swamps, so well adapted to tidal conditions.

FREEDOM OF MOVEMENT IN ANIMALS

Animals, too, no less than grasses, flowers, bushes, and trees, are directly influenced by the composition of the ground and the variety of its structural forms. These have largely helped to determine the distribution of living creatures right from the beginning of their existence on earth. In many places, particularly those where conditions are hardest and most extreme, they have produced in the land fauna characteristic 'ecological adaptations'. During the course of millions of years, the creatures that live above and below ground have developed many different modes of movement, each of them adapted to the structure of the ground which the creature concerned had to face: crawling, walking, running, jumping, climbing, and subterranean movement. In each instance, the development and anatomical construction of the organs of movement correspond to the use made of them.

Let us consider the horse. All the postulates for speed and endurance on resistant ground are present: power in the legs in spite of light build, simplified construction of the leg skeleton, making

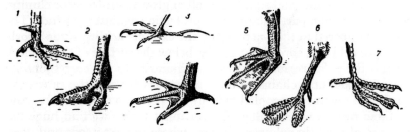

The adaptation of birds' feet to the structure of the ground. 1. For walking: chicken's foot. 2. For running: ostrich's foot. 3. For walking: skylark's foot. 4. For wading: stork's foot. 5. For paddling: pelican's foot. 6. For swimming: cloven foot of the crested diver. 7. For walking: pheasant's foot.

dislocation less likely, oblique-angled linkage of almost all the bones in the leg to give the best springing, and last but not least the perfect construction of the hoof. With the jutting edge of the horny shoe, particularly the front part of it, the horse braces itself against the

30

ground. The horse's single-toed foot is as well constructed for the hard ground of the steppes as it is ill adapted for soft going.

How closely the formation of the limbs can be adapted to the mode of life of their owners is convincingly demonstrated by the example of birds' feet. The differences in their structure become particularly clear if we compare the highly specialized foot of an African ostrich with that of a swift or a humming bird. The excellent development of the legs makes the ostrich into a swift and persevering runner thanks to the huge thigh muscles and the length of the stride. In addition, the ostrich has only two toes, the bigger of which is embedded in a sort of cushion and equipped with a hoof-like nail, while the upper surface of the toes and the front of the leg carry shields of horn. This highly specialized leg enables the bird to run across hot desert ground whether it is rocky, sandy or even littered with sharp splinters of stone. The ostrich can run at thirty miles an hour; at this speed, every stride carries it forward four yards. On the other hand, swifts, which spend almost their whole life in the air, can no longer walk at all and have turned their atrophied 'walking tools' into sharp-clawed 'hands' with which they cling on to steeply jutting rocks when they take a short rest or fly up to their nests. Both developments represent extreme specialization.

No other group of vertebrates is literally so close to the ground as snakes. The lengthening of their bodies must be regarded as a consequence of the mode of locomotion of their ancestors, which are to be sought among the lizards and which wound their way over the ground with horizontal twists of their bodies, as some members of the various families of reptiles still do today. Other concomitants of this method of movement are the loss of limbs and the elasticity of the jaw and trunk, so important for the swallowing and digestion of food.

Perfect adaptation to the surface of the ground is displayed by the slug. In crawling, it never lifts its muscular 'foot' from the ground and leaves behind on its path a gleaming trail of slime. This stream of slime, which is produced by a gland in the foot and runs under the sole, smoothes out all irregularities in the ground and remains stuck to it. Thus the sole of the foot never makes direct contact with the ground, but only with the strip of slime. As a result, for all practical purposes the surface is always the same, and the animal can move equally well on firm or loose soil. Indeed, a slug could crawl over the edge of a razor blade without hurting itself in the least.

In beetles, too, the anatomy of the legs is extensively adapted to the prevailing character of the ground. We meet ordinary legs

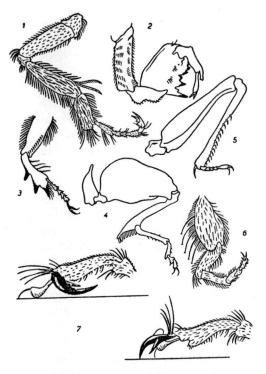

Insects' Legs—Changing and Changeable

1. *Back leg of the furry bee* Anthophora, *a typical 'shin-bone gatherer', as opposed to our honey bee, which is a 'thigh-gatherer'.*
2. *Scraping leg of a cicada larva* (Magicicada).
3. *Digging leg of a cockchafer* (Melolontha).
4. *Jumping leg of the* Psylliodes, *a leaf beetle.*
5. *Jumping leg of a locust* (Dissosteira).
6. *Leg of the silverfish* (Lepisma).
7. *Position of the bottom foot joint of the honey bee, above on a smooth below on a rough surface.*

designed for walking or adhesion—the latter equipped with sticky feet for climbing; middle pairs of legs developed for running and pushing; back legs designed for jumping; and front legs clearly adapted for digging. On the whole, beetles tread on the whole foot, and are therefore plantigrades, unlike their grubs, which walk on their claws, or spiders, which only touch the ground with the tips of their feet. Often the soles of the feet are equipped with adhesive hairs or bristles for climbing, which permit movement on very smooth, steep or even overhanging surfaces. The direct influence exerted by the size of the soil particles on soil organisms was demonstrated by a series of experiments with sand grains of different sizes on beetles of the genus *Bembidion*. Individual species of this genus prefer different substrata; the preference may be for gravel, for coarse, medium or fine sand, for clay or for loam. It is known that cockchafers seek out loose soil that warms up easily in which to lay their eggs.

It is evident from what has been said already that there are close connections between shape of body, mode of locomotion, and

Moulded by wind and water in the course of many thousands of years, these huge towers of rock rise out of the plains in Monument Valley (Utah, U.S.A.) like stone temples. (Photo: Domnick-Film/DFH.)

character of the soil. A few particularly characteristic examples from extremely dry and extremely wet regions will make these connections still clearer.

In the desert, the loose sand and rounded or sharp-edged fragments and splinters of stone offer no purchase to the limbs of heavy animals. In addition, during the course of the day the ground often attains a glowing heat. Yet in spite of its own weight and the loads it carries the camel strides confidently over the hot ground with a light, elastic step. This is only possible because its deeply cloven feet are equipped with hard-skinned, springy, cushion-like pads, which form broad surfaces, so that the animal does not need to fear soft, sandy or sharp ground. Similar structural peculiarities, which do much to prevent sinking in the sand, are exhibited by other animals that live on sandy ground. For instance, desert larks are characterized by broadened feet, while sand grouse have plenty of feathers on the shank and toes, and jumping rats have hairs along the sides of the soles of their feet.

Similar arrangements are found in desert lizards, especially in the gecko of the Namib Desert in South Africa, which has developed regular webbing between the toes. The loose and shifting texture of sand has produced its own particular type of 'sand-swimmers', which move immediately under the surface in such a way that the hole they make closes up behind them again at once. These include the European sand-snake and above all the skink, with its pointed snout. These burrowing lizards show such a marked capacity to dig themselves swiftly into the sand and to 'swim' through it that they have been nicknamed 'sand-fish'. The fringe-toed lizard of the Sahara possesses a comb-shaped line of projecting scales on the toes which help to enlarge the upper surface of the toes, thus preventing the animal sinking into the loose sand.

No less excellently equipped for life in the desert are Egyptian horned vipers. The scales along each side of their bodies stick out like a sort of saw-edged keel. When the viper shakes its body from side to side, these scales shovel the sand from underneath over its body, so that the animal slowly sinks into the sand. To protect them from the sand, horned vipers have a kind of flap in their noses, and can shut their lips exceptionally tight. In order to get a grip with its

---

Sand, rocks, and dry vegetation characterize the desert. Exceptional conditions have produced exceptional forms of life.—The grandiose landscape of the Siberian taiga: marshes, forests, and lakes as far as the eye can see. (Aerial photograph.) (Photos: Ullstein Picture Service.)

belly on the smooth, loose sand, which offers about as much resistance as a sheet of glass, the sidewinder rattlesnake, like the vipers described above, has to arrange its body in several successive S-bands, which give each other mutual support. In crawling, the weight of the animal's body can press only downwards, for the bends prevent it slipping sideways.

Similar modifications designed to cope with desert conditions, the high temperature, the extreme aridity and above all the exceptional nature of the soil are also displayed by the *Tenebrionidae*, the black beetles of the desert. With them the changes consist partly of the development of the forelegs into regular digging tools, and

Sternodes, *a black beetle that inhabits the desert. The tips of its legs have been developed into regular 'sand-shoes' in the form of long claws trimmed with bristles.*

partly of a lengthening of the legs as a whole, as a result of which, as in the case of water-boatmen, the body's weight is distributed over a greater area, friction is increased, and at the same time contact between the torso and the hot desert soil is avoided as far as possible. Other desert *Tenebrionidae* have developed the tips of their legs into 'sand shoes'—that is, long claws bordered with bristles which make it impossible for the insect to sink into the sand. Centipedes living in the desert have developed long fringes on their feet.

We find similar adaptations in other animals that live on a loose surface and consequently must protect themselves against sinking in, but this time in a region that is the diametrical opposite of the desert. I am referring to the inhabitants of the mountains and the polar regions, for whom fine-grained powdery snow raises much the same problems as desert sand. The peculiar horny plates which broaden the toes of the grouse may certainly be regarded as 'snow-tyres'. The ptarmigan, various breeds of which occur in the Alps and the far north, also has feathers on its legs and toes. In the case of the

34

alpine hare, hairs on the soles of the feet help to prevent it sinking in. In fact a closely related species in North America is known as the 'snow-shoe rabbit'.

Animals which dwell among steep rocks and smooth, loose boulders have found perfect solutions to the problem of slipping. Surprising climbing ability is shown by the geckos, thanks to the adhesive apparatus on the underside of the toes. This apparatus consists of thin, blade-like pieces of skin, containing innumerable, microscopically small, hook-shaped cells which grip the slightest unevennesses in the ground. When the foot presses down, these sticky cushions also act as suction-cups, so that a gecko can walk perfectly well on the ceiling.

The broad-footed pouched mice of Australia are outstanding climbers. The pads of these tiny mouse-like predatory marsupials are equipped with sticky ridges which enable them to scale the steepest cliffs. The rock cavy, a species of guinea-pig found in many parts of South America, is adapted to living among the stones and rocks of the mountain wildernesses through the development of thick balls on its toes and claws that broaden out like cups. Wherever there are rocky landscapes in Africa one finds the hyrax, even sometimes at a height of ten thousand feet. These curious ungulates, which are distantly related to the elephant but look like little marmots, display masterly skill in moving about the rocks. They can run up and down almost perpendicular rock faces, and climb up and down cracks and crevices with incredible agility. They are enabled to do this by the curious but most appropriate configuration of the soles of their feet, which are hairless and equipped with several very pliable horny cushions separated from each other by deep hollows. These soft yet rough cushions fulfil the same function as the 'sticky fingers' of the tree frog and the gecko: in climbing, the sole is first pressed down, then drawn up, so that a vacuum is produced underneath it. In addition, the sole is always kept tacky by a rich secretion of sweat.

Other animals whose legs and feet are perfectly adapted to their environment are the big mountain-dwellers like the mountain sheep, the wild goat, and the chamois. These animals are strikingly well equipped for a life which seems to defy the laws of gravity. The chamois and its Asiatic relatives, the serow and the goral, have widely extendible, sharp-edged hoofs, and provide man with a perfect illustration of how to protect the soles of his feet and stop them slipping. The model of these hoofs has been followed from the days of old Chinese bad-weather shoes and Roman legionary sandals right up to modern boots for mountaineering expeditions.

The rock kangaroo is, so to speak, the chamois of Australia. Another animal that is quite at home among rocks is the klipspringer (*Oreotragus saltator*); the slightest projection is enough to provide this species of antelope, found in all the mountain ranges of Africa, with a firm foothold. The connection between the surface of the ground and the development of the legs and feet is also made clear by the fact that malformations of the hoof soon occur in rock-dwelling ungulates when they are moved by man to environments that do not suit them. The best-known example of this is the lengthening and ingrowing of the hoofs of mountain sheep that had been shifted to flat land. In woodland there is no employment for the natural growth of the horn, and in spite of otherwise favourable conditions the claws become distorted and the pads diseased. It was necessary to catch the sheep and cut their claws, just as one does with tame goats and cattle, which display the same phenomena if they are kept in stalls all the time.

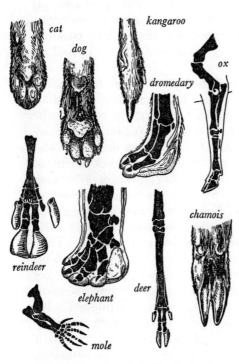

Varying Formation of the Feet in Land Animals

The firm, wide expanse of the steppe demands suitable adaptations in its inhabitants just as much as hard stone and rock do. The horse's hoof, which shows this adaptation in its most perfect form, has already been mentioned. The Australian bandicoot, too, is a genuine steppe-dweller and shows the characteristic coalescence of the second and third hind toes up to the nails, an adaptation found in numerous other natives of the steppe: jumping mice and kangaroos, for instance, and, above all, antelopes. Whether big or small, antelopes are all true animals of the steppe. Gracefully built, with a fragile-looking

36

gait and long, narrow, pointed hoofs, they can leap six feet into the air from a more or less standing start. When danger threatens, they shoot off with high yard-long leaps, their forelegs pressed close to their bodies, their hindlegs and heads stretched right out. A contrasting example of a steppe animal is the elephant, which in spite of its very heavy body walks as lightly as if it were on crêpe soles. The weight—on an average, three to four tons—is not borne, as it is in the typical ungulate, by the tips of the toes, which are protected by flat hoofs, but on a thick cushiony sole, which acts as an elastic shock-absorber. With feet like this, elephants on the steppe can cover thirty, forty, or even fifty miles a day without showing any signs of tiredness.

A noteworthy adaptation to the terrain of the steppe is displayed by the Australian flat-headed pouched mouse. Its head is curiously flattened in a way unparalleled among the mammals. This unusual flat head is not just a whim of nature; its biological significance is that it enables the animal to slip into the cracks and crevices of the dried-up savannah.

Living in marshy land is quite a different proposition to living on loose desert sand or the firm, hard ground of the steppe. Thus the marsh stag of South America has long, pointed hoofs, which are spread out wide when the animal is moving over boggy ground. The elk, too, has big, wide hoofs that can be spread out to prevent it sinking in. In the reindeer the same development has gone still further. Its spread hoofs, together with the broad dew claws, enable it to move easily and surely over the soft surface of the moors and snowfields of its homeland.

A similar line of development leads from the European wild boar to the hippopotamus, which can walk easily across marshes thanks to the broad surface of its extendible 'toes'. The arni-buffaloes that live in the marshy lowlands of eastern India and Indonesia are particularly well equipped for moving in mud. The very broad hoofs and relatively small decline of the dew claws prevent the heavy, unusually powerful bodies of these water buffaloes from sinking in too far. That is why they are the only animals that can pull a plough through the soft ground of the rice fields. Ideal adaptation to their marshy habitat can also be discerned in the curious feet of the marsh goats that live in the highlands of southern Ethiopia. Very long, slender, pointed hoofs crown very flexible toes, and the middle toes can be spread wide apart, so that when the animal walks the underside of the toes lies on the ground and the

37

backs of the hoofs touch the earth. The East African waterbuck is a creature of the open steppe, but curiously enough feels most at home on marshy ground; it always stays close to water, often stands knee-deep in mud and always flees in the direction of water. Its hoofs are exceptionally long and slender, and there is no hair between the dew claws and hoofs; both these details are typical adaptations to wet, marshy ground.

TIRELESS ROOTERS

The ground, both at the surface and below it, is subject to all kinds of mechanical interference from animal life. Large animals affect the ground by walking and grazing on it, and when they live in herds they very naturally produce considerable local changes. The effects produced by the activities of African big game—elephants, rhinoceroses, and buffaloes—when bathing and wallowing at their drinking places, and in the dry periods when digging for water, have often been vividly described by explorers, particularly in their accounts and explanations of the so-called 'salt pans' of the Kalahari, pools filled with calcareous tufa and now in the process of drying up. In general, animals which dwell in, hide in, or seek food in the ground can affect the texture of the local soil considerably. Very often they are 'scrapers'—that is, animals endowed with sharp claws or scraping ridges on their feet. Among these are the badger, hamster, weasel and prairie dog, and also the rush toad and sand martin.

Pigs, too, are rooters that disturb the soil, the African bush pig even more so than the European wild boar. Bush pigs live in big packs, and in their search for food they give the earth a regular ploughing. Warthogs, likewise natives of Africa, which live in small packs in caves or in the deserted burrows of aardvarks, or 'earth hogs', press down with their hindquarters and slide forward on the thick horny pads of their wrists when they are grubbing up roots and tubers from the earth with their barrel-shaped bodies. However, these horny pads are not an adaptation developed by digging; they are present in the young boars at birth. The omnivorous nature of the pig emerges clearly from the structure of the molars and also more particularly from the powerful development of the muscles in the nape of the neck and the fore part of the back. These muscles enable the animal to lift with its snout roots that a man could not tear out even with the aid of a crowbar.

With the help of their powerful claws the ant-eater, pangolin and armadillo dig for ants and termites. In these animals, differences

38

in physical shape, armour, and digging equipment all represent adaptations eminently suited to the kind of ground in which they dig. This is particularly obvious in the case of the fairy armadillo, a dwarf armadillo which lives in the driest areas of South America. The low-set, shield-shaped armour on the buttocks allows the animal to dig backwards as well in sandy soil; the very horny tail is then wrapped under the body and acts as a kind of anti-skid device. Above ground the fairy armadillo is hindered by its huge claws designed for digging, and is even more helpless than the 'tatu careta', as the natives call the giant armadillo.

The digging ability of the aardvark, or 'earth hog', which belongs to the ancient family of hollow-toothed animals and lives in the savannah and semi-deserts of Africa, is almost uncanny. The aardvark is a highly specialized termite-eating, burrowing, nocturnal creature, and has exceptionally strong, hoof-like claws for digging, which enable it to disappear into the earth amid a shower of stones and clods of earth almost before you can turn round. The degree to which the physical composition of the soil influences the selection, mode of life, and bodily shape of digging animals naturally depends mainly on whether they dig in the ground only occasionally, make burrows and runs in the earth regularly in their search for food and nesting places, or are permanent inhabitants of the existing underground network of pores and cavities.

Most cylindrical or barrel-shaped shovellers work their way through the soil with the aid of their legs. The most typical example of this class is the mole, which is known all over the world and displays almost perfect adaptation to underground activity in various different kinds of ground. In the mole, the legs, originally developed by mammals for walking, have become shovel-shaped, 'short-handled' digging tools, excellently adapted to scraping the earth loose and to pressing it into the sides of the tunnel or throwing it back. How successfully these tools are used can be clearly seen when the mole quickly digs itself into the ground and constructs the passages which man can only invade with the help of iron spades. The strong shovel-shaped hands are backed up by the conical head, which is driven into the soil like a wedge with powerful shoves. In hard or stony ground the mole is forced to draw its head in and to advance feet first. The long, uniformly strong body, quite free from any obstructive projections; the short hairs of the coat, which have no nap and thus make movement forward or backward equally convenient; the absence of external ears, which are superfluous in view of the excellent way the earth conducts sound; all these details are perfect adaptations to the special conditions and peculiarities of the subterranean realm.

Indeed it is the mole that has taught modern technology how best to move forwards through the earth. Men have built 'steel moles' for big boring operations such as installing heating pipes in a large district or laying subterranean cables. This torpedo-shaped machine, equipped with a high-speed drill at the tip and two rings of shovels at the side which press the excavated earth into the walls of the tunnel by hydraulic means, is working today, alongside the automatic pilot, the echo-sounder, and the gyro-compass, in the service of technology.

To return to animals, we find the digging work of the legs backed up by the pushing and boring of the head in the golden mole and the marsupial mole as well as in the European species. But in instances where the front legs have not been converted into shovels, as in the case of the European shrew, either the passages are very close to the surface of the ground or the animal prefers to use existing mole-runs or cracks and clefts in the ground.

Forefoot of the badger, a typical 'scraper', underside.

A creature that is remarkably specialized and particularly well adapted to its subterranean life is the Central African shrew. Its special vertebrae are fastened together by interlocking teeth into a sort of girder strong enough to withstand pressure from above when the shrew is in its run just under the surface of the ground.

The curiously shaped 'horned toad' makes use of its unusually flat body to dig itself into the sand with a peculiar shovelling movement. The animal bends one side of its body down and with it tips sand over its back, then does the same with the other side. These movements proceed without a stop and the lizard literally sinks into the ground before the onlooker's eye. Reptiles, with their various ways of digging and burrowing, always provide informative and interesting examples of adaptation to the prevailing properties of the soil.

We also find evidence of adaptation in many species of insects which dig passages in the ground, go down deeper to lay their eggs, or burrow in dung heaps and similar things. For example, there is the European mole-cricket, with its barrel-shaped body covered in fine hairs, its compact, strong, shovel-like forelegs, and the strikingly big thorax enclosing the muscles of the digging tools. The main work in digging is probably carried out by the shovel-shaped, flattened shin, which is equipped with pointed teeth for excavating and embodies the principle of the short lever exerting the maximum force. The broad, toothed shins found in the forelegs of many beetles, especially horn beetles, confirm that these extremities have to do the job of digging and scraping. The forelegs of dung beetles are typical examples: to the hips and powerful thighs are fastened the shins, broadened out like shovels at the lower ends. On the outside these shins have strong, downward-pointing teeth, and on the inside of the ends dagger-shaped bent spurs. Similar formations can be observed in many ground beetles. On the other hand, curiously enough, there are also many species which can dig very well although outwardly they show no signs of corresponding changes in their limbs.

Highly specialized legs for digging are possessed by many tropical insects, which live in little tunnels they have made themselves and suck at roots. This is particularly true of a species from Guatemala, which may perhaps be regarded as the most extreme example there is of a mining insect. Its head is rimmed like a shovel, its antennae are protected by a shield, the forelegs have been converted into pick-axes, the middle legs are adapted to pushing sideways and backwards, the back legs have been turned into heavy rams, the torso is barrel-shaped, the armour is tough, and the bristles slope backward. All these details add up to a perfectly designed digging and burrowing machine.

Among other animals that affect the structure of the ground there are also some that dig with their teeth and only use their legs for pushing. The best-known examples are the voles and the blind mole, which both work primarily with their powerfully developed teeth. The European vole—the biggest of the voles—digs passages just below the surface of the ground. The resulting heaps of earth are distinguished from those of the mole mainly by the fact that they consist partly of coarse, uncrushed material. On the steppes of the southern Urals the ground was found to be riddled with vole-runs down to a depth of fifteen feet. It is only these tunnels that enable roots of certain plants to gain access to the deeper levels of soil containing plenty of water.

From time to time there are plagues of voles, as there are of lemmings, and these plagues are much feared. In these 'vole years' there can be twenty or thirty thousand voles on a couple of acres of land! With some of these rodents, the colonies are so close to each other that the whole ground is riddled with tunnels over a wide area. This also happens with the little guinea-pigs that live in huge colonies

in the deserts of South America; with the crested rats of the Cordilleras; and with the viscachas, also natives of South America, which
live in a maze of communal underground burrows that they share
with snakes and owls.

Mole-cricket (Gryllotalpa) *in its tunnel. On the right, the
shovel-shaped leg for digging.*

Marsupial rats, which are almost as big as hamsters, belong to the
same category; they feed mainly on roots, and in order to get at
these they make their tunnels just below the surface of the ground.
They use their upper incisors like mattocks to loosen up the soil, and
their front feet for digging and shovelling. A curious kind of dia-
phragm divides the mouth into two, giving the lower incisors freedom
of movement for gnawing and at the same time preventing earth
and particles of wood from reaching the back of the mouth.

In the case of the mole-rats, whose life is completely subterranean,
the curious line of bristles running diagonally from the corner of the
mouth across the cheeks is simply set against the earth, which is then
pushed aside by the swift raising and lowering of the creature's
head. The feet and claws, to judge by their poor development, play
scarcely any part in the process. The jerboa, or 'jumping mouse',
from the deserts of North Africa digs for roots and insects with the
sharp nails of its front feet, and uses its molars for breaking up hard
bits of soil. In the sandy coastal regions of South Africa lives the fat,
barrel-shaped beach-digger, a short-legged creature which seizes
big lumps of earth with its molars and thus loosens up the soil. The
loose material is pushed by the forefeet, with their big, sharp nails,

42

to the hindfeet, which then send it further back. The kingfisher uses both beak and feet to make its long tunnels in river banks; these tunnels open out at the end like caves, and there the bird lays its eggs on a bed of regurgitated fishbones and indigestible fragments of insects.

In a number of beetles, such as the mud beetle, which lives in passages in sandy and muddy river banks and other damp places, the greatly enlarged upper jaw takes over the job of digging and the powerfully developed legs act as braces or supports. Other creatures which dig with their mouths are 'wire-shaped' click-beetle larvae and the larvae of the *Cicindela*, which dig long, steep tunnels in sandy ground and cling to the walls with the aid of a fork in the back. Ants, too, fall into the same category; many species, as is well known, are capable of carrying out extensive and deep burrowing operations. If the soil is loose and can be worked fairly easily, the jaws are employed in the closed position as shovels, but the jaws also serve as pincers for loosening, grasping, and carrying away particles of earth. The forelegs, too, are used as digging tools. For digging in loose sand, which is difficult to carry, ants have bristles arranged like baskets on the front edge of the head and on the underside of the jaw and head. These are used for moving and carrying off loose sand.

Small Rodents
1. *Lemming* (Myodes lemmus).
2. *Jerboa or jumping mouse* (Dipus aegypticus).

Many land animals work their way through the ground by means of peristaltic contractions of the body. This method of movement is particularly characteristic of the class which digs by boring. A considerable number of the skinks, which we have already mentioned, show a certain degree of atrophy in the legs, so that for practical purposes these subterranean lizards have only one tool at their disposal for digging, namely the head, which has to be forced straight through the ground with the help of the muscular body. As a result, most of the skinks have developed decidedly conical heads; in some species the process has gone so far that the snout sticks right out like a pointed thorn. Generally the lower jaw then fits so closely into the upper jaw that it is scarcely perceptible in the silhouette of the skull. The lizard's skull is all the better adapted as a boring tool that has to

43

overcome the resistance of the ground by the fact that the scales on the head, thanks to their striking size and stiff arrangement, form a sort of protective, stabilizing sheath.

There is also a close connection between the shape of the head and the method of digging in the amphisbaenas, which are mostly found in the tropics. The majority of them have blunt heads, but some species possess flattened, wedge-shaped snouts which are particularly well adapted to burrowing in hard ground. Analogous adaptations to a subterranean, burrowing mode of life are also displayed by slow-worms and burrowing snakes. In the former, the mechanical employment of the skull has led to many of the bones in the skull coalescing, so that the structure of the skull is considerably strengthened. Many burrowing snakes, which push their heads forward and then turn them from side to side, are characterized not only by massively constructed heads but also by strikingly well-developed muscles in the nape of the neck.

Many of the adders are typical diggers. Those that live underground have particularly smooth scales and a completely round body. The number of scales—and therefore the friction—has also been reduced. There are further differentiations according to whether the creatures live in loose sandy ground, heavy soil, or damp earth. In some of these land snakes the head is like a wedge-shaped chisel and in others like a carinate beak. Adders with blunt, rounded heads made for boring live in the relatively moist ground of rain forests, which consists of rotted vegetation, while the chisel-nosed burrowers are at home in savannahs and deserts, since they are in a position to penetrate the hard ground. Finally, among the adders with the most highly perfected poison mechanisms, we find highly specialized underground burrowers: these are the earth vipers which occur in most parts of Africa between the Sahara and the Cape. Like other burrowing snakes, they have round bodies, very narrow heads, tiny eyes, and shortened tails characteristic of an underground mode of life, but they possess a relatively large number of rows of scales. They feed for the most part on small mammals, attacking and catching them in their underground dwellings.

Other 'borers' are the exclusively tropical blind-voles, some amphibians with worm-shaped bodies and completely atrophied extremities, and of course earthworms. These last move by alternately stretching and contracting their bodies, especially the front end of them. The backward-sloping bristles prevent the worm from slipping backwards when it contracts. The bristles must be regarded as the

44

remains of a more substantial organ of movement. Some of the earthworm's marine relatives, the polychaetes or bristle-worms, still possess whole bundles of often quite substantial bristles, which are usually arranged on flaps of skin, like oars. In the earthworm, however, the bristles are only in pairs. In loose soil, the muscular, awl-shaped head bores into the ground and, since the head is expanded at the same time, the loosened particles of earth are pressed to the side. Where the ground is firmer, the earthworm makes its little tunnels by swallowing the earth, which passes through the gut and is then either deposited on the surface (worm casts) or used to line and smooth the tunnels. Movement in the tunnels is effected by the muscles of the skin, the body being inflated at the same time, so that the bristles can be used as supports on the walls.

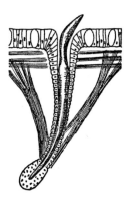

Bristle of an earthworm in its natural position. It sits in a pocket of skin and is moved by special bands of muscles.

It is fairly obvious that the mechanical working of the soil by animals is important in the loosening-up and manuring of the ground, and that their digging and burrowing activities influence the growth of vegetation. They help to aerate and irrigate the ground. The loosening-up of the soil allows the roots of plants to push deeper and the nutriment available is put to the best possible use. In one square yard of field one could often count hundreds of earthworm tunnels traversing the topsoil in every direction and, below the surface, leading perpendicularly down.

Amazing movements of soil, especially in steppe regions, are due to the activity of rodents. Among them there are diggers and burrowers which can manage with a minimum of oxygen and are extremely insensitive to extremes of temperature. The mole-rats of the African deserts dig just below the surface of the loose sand in the scorching midday sun; arctic lemmings go on unconcernedly building their nests and tunnels in the icy polar cold. For years observers have watched the effect of pouched rats, which are capable of shifting many tons of earth per square mile every year, on vegetation, and noted that shrubs with woody roots derive considerable advantage from their activities, while plants with fleshy roots tend to wither away.

There are inveterate burrowers among the marsupials, most of whom are confined to Australia. The little marsupial shrew burrows

45

in the leaf mould of the Amazonian forest; the blind marsupial marmot moves easily in sandy ground with the aid of its strong digging claws. Long-eared marsupial badgers construct burrows and underground systems of passages many feet deep, while the low-slung wombat with its sickle-shaped claws builds underground passages up to thirty yards long. In thick undergrowth and above all in marshy ground, bush kangaroos, which are the size of a hare, make passages like tunnels through which they can visit their feeding places unobserved.

On the Kalmuck steppe, between the Volga and the Don, ground squirrels bring up from as deep as fifteen feet tens of thousands of cubic yards of earth per square mile every year. The earth thus brought up is first colonized by weeds, which gradually make way for grass again.

In savannah and steppe regions termites can positively transform the appearance of the landscape. In the neighbourhood of their nests they loosen up the hard, crusted soil, drain it, manure it, and create a mild humus which gives rise to small wooded 'islands' in the midst of a 'sea' of grass. On marshy subsoils, through their manifold organic mining activities, they are capable of creating out of fruit, carrion, and so forth fertile ground that can be used for farming. In many regions of Africa cultivation of the soil is restricted to patches of fertile ground created in this way by the activities of termites. The materials used in the above-ground galleries of the termites' constructions are washed away in the rainy season and thus returned to the soil. Many species of termites build ingenious nests that go deep into the ground; in some respects they are extremely complicated, with multiple walls and millions of tiny holes for ventilation. Some species build perpendicular air shafts which reach up to the surface of the ground. On the other hand, other species of subterranean termites do without a proper nest and live in a maze of branching passages. The termites of southern Europe, like the tropical ones, live in self-made tunnels, eating their way through the soil like earthworms. Many species build covered runs and tunnels on the surface of the ground.

Ants play quite an important part in soil biology; their precise effect on the structure of the soil depends on the nature of the nest. Species that live in the ground dig shallow, thinly populated tunnels; other species build loose mounds of earth on the surface. These mounds are usually braced with stems of plants and pine needles. Such tunnels and mounds clearly loosen up the soil; in addition,

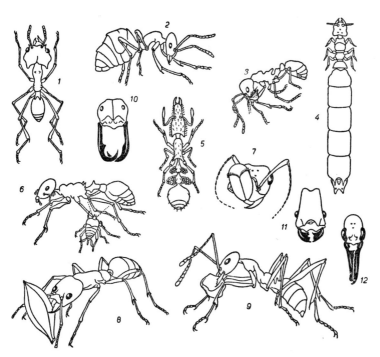

Various ants and their different modes of life. 1. Soldier ant from Africa. 2. Chilean desert ant. 3. Ant with Antennophorus *mite, which perches like a muzzle close behind the host's mouth (commensal relation). 4. Wingless female wandering ant. 5. Extreme form of a tropical species that lives in the ground. 6. Ant-cricket on an ant's leg. 7. Tiny beetle on an ant's feeler. 8. Corn-ant. 9. Steppe ant, which builds a nest like a crater and often penetrates down to deposits of ore. 10–12. Heads of various soldier ants.*

the fully underground nests cause an extensive mixing of organic and inorganic materials. This can involve quite considerable movements of earth; it is known that some species bring to the surface every year over ten pounds of earth per square yard. Thus in dry soil where there are no earthworms, or only very few, ants can take over their rôle. In hot, dry regions, some species of ants go down as far as the water table for their water supplies. For instance, the breeding places of leaf-cutting ants lie on an average five feet down; other species go as much as fifteen or even thirty feet deep. It is obvious that the activity of all these ants results in a considerable rearrangement of the soil. The amount of soil brought out by a Brazilian leaf-cutting species has been estimated at three hundred cubic yards, and the number of individuals in the colony concerned at half a

47

million at the least! From the nests, well-cared-for paths, always kept scrupulously clean, lead, sometimes over great distances, to the collecting places. The entrances to a nest of leaf-cutting ants can lie over a hundred yards apart. A whole system of traffic arteries, perpendicular ventilation shafts, and radial passages for moving material leads to the centres of the subterranean network. A space of nine to ten cubic yards, going down to a depth of seven to ten feet, is divided into thousands of chambers, each of them about four inches in diameter.

Ants also work in marshy land: notched and bog ants build their nests on little cushions of moss, piling up little bits of moss and plant which they have bitten off. In course of time these ant-hills become more and more overgrown with vegetation, gradually counteract the marshiness of the ground, and thanks to the lowering of the soil's acidity—a process also largely due to the ants—form the foundation on which a higher vegetation can flourish.

Desert and steppe ants construct crater-shaped nests, with a shaft going straight down into the ground, often as deep as twenty feet. Ants in the desert regions of Chile go right down to the deep-lying veins of copper, silver, and gold; this explains the discovery of gold-bearing grains of sand in their craters. In the mountains of Florida the course of the veins of manganese has often been established with the help of the soil ejected from ants' nests.

That the activity of ants causes a considerable rearrangement of the soil is even true in those cases where ants site their nests under flat stones. Through the continual clearing-away of the soil the stone sinks deeper and deeper into the earth. In addition, the constituents of old ants' nests are spread out all over the surrounding neighbourhood by burrowing mice and scratching birds, as well as by wind and water, and thus serve to improve the humus. This is the only way in which we can explain how it is that in areas once inhabited by ants grass, shrubs, bushes, and trees all grow with particular luxuriance.

On the other hand, in certain circumstances ants' nests can also help to damage vegetation. To give their nests the requisite amount of sun, many ants will not tolerate any plants in the immediate neighbourhood, or only those whose seeds they gather. North

A well-preserved fossil from the Posidonia Beds of Holzmaden in Württemberg: Teleosaurus bollensis, *a prehistoric crocodile-like reptile,* 10 *feet long (Geological and Paleontological Museum, Tübingen.)*

48

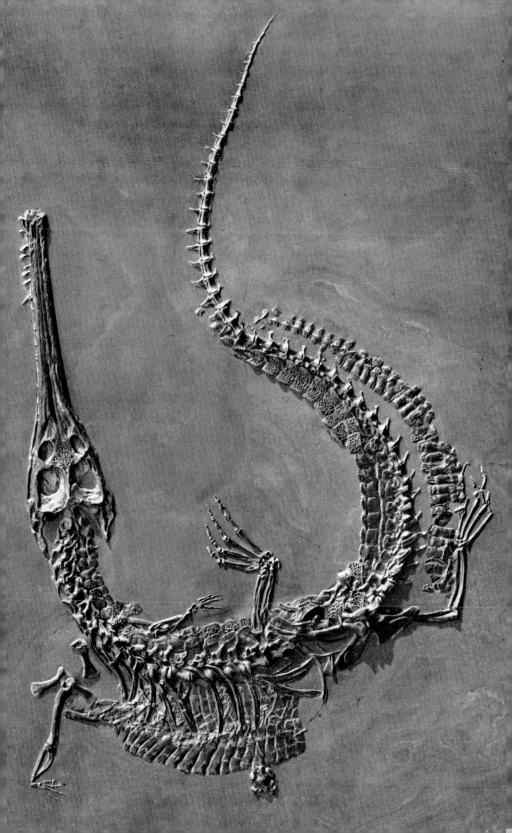

American harvest ants gnaw holes above ground level in the bark of all the trees near their nests and inject acid into them. As a result, the liquid in the sap-wood runs away and the flow of sap to the roots is halted. The trees die and the sunshine has free access to the nest.

It would be possible to cite many other examples of the detrimental effect on vegetation of land animals that dig or burrow. Barking squirrels' burrows are marked by a curious arrangement of the vegetation in zones: round the opening the ground is bare and churned up; farther off there is a little grass, which gradually becomes more luxuriant until it merges into the original long grass of the prairie. It is the same with rabbit warrens, especially in sand dunes, where the digging activities of the rabbits set in motion the drifting sand which has been held to some extent by the vegetation. This can result in the production of shifting dunes.

INTERNAL SYSTEM OF CAVITIES IN THE SOIL

Factors such as capacity for air and water and conditions of warmth and light, so important to all plant and animal life, are decisively affected, if not determined, by the micro-crumbling—the fine structural breaking-down—of the ground. Detailed comparative investigations of the volume of cavities in different areas of soil have shown that at least a third, and usually a half and more, of the volume of the soil consists of cavities. The rhizosphere—the upper layer traversed by roots—displays the greatest percentage of cavities; ploughland is usually poorer in cavities than grassland. The coarse cavities—the ones over 30 microns wide—allow ventilation of the soil; the medium-sized cavities (5 to 30 microns) serve to conduct water; the finest holes hold the ground-water, thus forming the real water-reservoir for all life in the soil. Good crumbly soil which has been well and truly broken down is distinguished by optimum structural conditions; that is, the coarse, medium, and fine cavities are present in approximately equal proportions.

The effect of the system of cavities is by no means confined to water capacity and the conduction of heat; it also embraces habitability by the various organisms living in the ground, which display many adaptations to the physical properties of their fine-meshed environment. The inhabitants of the soil include creatures that are more or

---

A dwarf among mammals: the harvest mouse, which is less than three inches long. It builds its nest, which is like a little round ball, in bushes and reeds. (Photo: Harald Doering.)

D

less spherical in shape, like many beetles and mites. A characteristically disc-shaped form occurs in various species of snail that live in the soil. Sphincter-mouthed snails, insect larvae in quivers, leaf-beetle larvae, and the caterpillars of various moths are decidedly barrel-shaped or spindle-shaped.

Other inhabitants of the soil are distinguished by a noteworthy springiness that enables them to avoid external shocks in the soil. Many bugs, beetles, mites, and wingless tropical grasshoppers are also enabled by smooth body surfaces and a spherical shape to slip neatly into cracks and crevices in the ground. Numerous creatures that live in the ground possess a house into which they can withdraw;

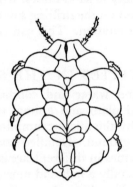

The shield-louse Orthezia. The surface of the body of this creature, which lives mostly underground on roots, is completely covered with hard, snow white, wax plates.

others can roll themselves up. Some of them have very prickly bodies, for instance the shield-louse (*Orthezia*), which is armoured with wax plates, and various moss mites.

Creatures that hide in cracks are usually strikingly flat in shape; this is also true of many bugs, some kinds of beetles, centipedes, and the larvae of flies. The tiny bristle-tails, earwigs, and the widely distributed short-winged beetles all possess a flexibility that allows them to find their way through the narrowest and most crooked passages. As well as ants, numerous gall-flies and ichneumon flies, bee-ants, and spiders are dumb-bell-shaped and distinguished by great nimbleness. Various club-beetles and ant-beetles, too, and not least the pseudo-scorpions, are shaped strikingly like ants.

The close relationship between the size of the cavities in the soil and the creatures that inhabit them becomes clear if we compare the mites which live in dense, loamy soil with those that live in loose layers of earth. Most of the former are small and light in colour, while the latter are generally bigger and more strongly coloured.

50

Besides these inhabitants of the soil which crawl, wind, or hop about in the bigger cavities and crevices, there are the organisms which live in the films of water on particles of soil and in the tiniest water-filled cracks and crevices. They occupy a rather special position. These algae, flagellata, ciliata, tardigrades (water-bears), rotifers, and threadworms, which swim about in water, form the living community of the lower edaphon.

The term 'edaphon' was first employed by Raoul H. Francé more than forty years ago in order to draw attention to the fact that, just as there is plankton in water, so too in the ground there are vegetable and animal organisms living and working together in a community. For all of them the porosity of the soil is of the greatest importance, for the size of their living space depends on the volume of the cavities in the ground. Muddy soil will naturally offer no possibility of life for a considerable proportion of the edaphic micro-organisms, except perhaps bacteria. Firmly compressed soil contains little air, but there are anaerobic species of bacteria which do not require oxygen. Where the structure of the soil is coarser and bacteria live alongside rotifers, threadworms, infusoria, and other micro-organisms, a healthy and harmonious balance of opposites prevails. The more 'crumbly' the soil is, so that all kinds of organisms with different needs can live together, the more 'active' it is.

Most of the edaphic organisms are adapted to the physical qualities of their living space, which is usually full of fine pores, by the possession of a fairly marked spherical or elliptical shape, which facilitates their ceaseless gliding to and fro. In the narrow confines of the tiny cracks in the earth the most varied methods of movement have been developed, from the restless twitching of the cocci and other bacteria to the smooth gliding of the land amoebas.

The structural complication and the functional mechanism of the cilia and flagella in the tiniest of some protozoa are amazing. Whether they appear singly or in 'partnerships' of closely united, sometimes agglutinate, organelles (cilia-fields, stiff tufts, clusters of flagella), they are ideal organs for swimming, jumping, steering, braking, and feeling. Besides the active propulsion provided by flagella and cilia in the flagellata and infusoria, there is another factor whose importance for swimming in the tiny cavities and water capillaries should not be underestimated, and that is the mainly passive 'conductibility' of the cell body. There are also cases where the bodies of the ciliata, and more particularly of the flagellata, have a screw shape. Here, in a hundred variations, is the principle of the ship's screw and the turbine.

This restless movement in the earth breaks up and loosens the tight structure of the soil and gives it, in a minute and hardly imaginable way, a microscopically fine texture. It is a significant part of the great process of the formation of humus.

3 *Life and Temperature*

CLIMATE—CONTINENTAL AND LOCAL

Not all climates are equally favourable to vegetable and animal life. Species which are a match for the inclemency of the climate often attain high numbers, as is shown by the colonies of rodents on the steppes and the hordes of voles and lemmings in the northern tundra. Relative uniformity occurs only in the tropical rain forests, because there temperature and moisture are fairly constant throughout the year.

The structure of the landscape and in particular the nature of the vegetation give rise to individual climates of a local nature, special climates which suit quite different animals and thus indirectly help to determine their distribution. The micro-climatic conditions in a damp, deciduous forest, on a heath, a high-lying moor, in reed banks or sand dunes can show quite considerable differences even when these regions belong to the same general climatic area. For example, the daily variations in air and ground temperature and in the humidity of the air are noticeably smaller in forests than in open spaces, where radiation is greater and wind and rain can exert their full effect. Daily and seasonal fluctuations in temperature and moisture can very well be modified by luxuriant vegetation. All these different factors produce specific individual and local climates. Because of their large water content and usually thick vegetation, marshes and bogs are marked by high humidity. Animals that like warmth penetrate farthest up into the mountains in areas that are well exposed to the sun. The insects that live on dry grassland are quite different from those that live in damp meadows.

Particularly extreme variations, which naturally have a noteworthy effect on the development and behaviour of organisms living above and below the surface of the ground, are found in the microclimate of the layer of air close to the ground.

The temperature of the air is most strongly affected in the neighbourhood of the ground; it is only there that most of the sun's radiation is absorbed and converted into heat. As a result, the temperature of the ground rises, and the less obliquely the radiation strikes it, the sharper the rise is. A film of air over the ground—a film that is only a few millimetres thick—quickly assumes the temperature of the soil, but since air is a poor conductor of heat this warmth rises very slowly and is eventually removed by convection. In windy weather the air close to the ground is continually renewed, and consequently no rise in temperature worth mentioning can take place; when there is no wind, on the other hand, or only a light breeze, the film of air over the ground can become considerably overheated before rising and being replaced by cooler air. As a result of the difference in the refraction of light between the consequent rising warm air and the surrounding and sinking colder air, streaks appear—they can be seen on any hot summer day as a sort of shimmer above the surface, especially over stony ground.

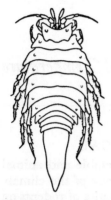

Mesidothea entomon, an isopod from the cold, damp ground of the Arctic. This is an example of a localized post-Ice Age relic.

The adaptation of vegetable and animal life to the climatic, and in particular thermal, peculiarities of its habitat makes it possible sometimes to speak of 'bioclimatic index forms', which often provide a more reliable picture of the effective environmental factors than measuring instruments can. Grasshoppers, cicadas, spiders, and snails are particularly useful in this respect. The climatic conditions determined by temperature and moisture can be quite different for a beetle larva boring under the bark of a tree trunk or in the timber itself, according to whether the trunk stands on the edge or in the interior of a wood, in the sun or in the shade. Creatures that live in the ground can create a particular micro-climate within their nests. For instance, a thirty-two-inch-deep nest of red forest ants has a temperature ten inches under the surface three to four degrees higher—on the sunny side, eight to twelve degrees higher—than the

54

surrounding air. It is precisely the favourable micro-climate in the depths of their nests that enables ants in temperate and cold climates to withstand the winter. In many cases, too, the association between ants and other small creatures, especially beetles, is almost certainly initiated by the attraction of the micro-climate of ants' nests.

The nature of the soil, its covering of vegetation, and the circumstances of the terrain have a far-reaching effect on the ground climate. Under the influence of daily and seasonal factors, there are naturally greater thermal fluctuations on the surface of the ground than in its interior. These variations in temperature grow progressively smaller with increasing depth; beyond a depth of four inches the soil shows a more nearly constant temperature. At times of maximum heat—during the daytime in the summer months—the ground absorbs great quantities of heat, which it gives off again during the night.

The height of the ground temperature depends on a number of different factors. As we have already said, the greatest influence is exerted by the climate of the layer of air next to the ground. In addition, wet ground warms and cools down more slowly than dry ground, and dark soil gets hotter than light soil. A coarse consistency and loose texture cause the top layer of soil to dry quickly. There are noteworthy differences, so far as the temperatures of the surface and top layers of soil are concerned, between ground with no vegetation—or very little—and ground protected against both irradiation and emission of heat by a continuous covering of vegetation. The latter shows much flatter daily and yearly temperature curves than the former, a circumstance that naturally has considerable influence on the selection and distribution of organisms, particularly those that live in the upper layers of the soil.

HEAT AND COLD AS GUIDING FORCES

We may assume that temperature is the most important of all the environmental factors that determine the ecological distribution of animals. The reason for this is that the biochemical processes in an organism are to a certain extent dependent on temperature and many of them can only function properly within a certain range of temperature. An excess of heat or cold alters or disturbs life in all its various forms and survival then necessitates regulation by means of special biological arrangements.

Many insects in temperate or cold regions pupate in the autumn and emerge as perfect insects in the spring.

55

Uniform body temperatures are maintained in warm-blooded animals by the exceptionally thorough assimilation of food. This liberates more energy than is needed for movement, nervous activity and so on, and by means of certain special arrangements this superfluous heat is kept at approximately the same level. Among these arrangements is an intensification of the oxidation processes in the body, so that the glycogen stored mainly in the liver and muscles is more thoroughly consumed; assistance is often provided by involuntary movements of the muscles (trembling). The size of the blood vessels, the heart beat, and the rate of breathing can also be altered. Overheating can be compensated for by sweating since evaporation of sweat helps to cool the body.

Loss of body heat is also noticeably reduced by a coat of hair or feathers. Adaptations of this sort, which make warm-blooded animals to a large extent physiologically independent of outside temperatures, undoubtedly made an essential contribution to the conquest of polar and mountainous regions by land animals.

In addition, many of them have developed special adaptations to the temperature. In this connection the relation of the body temperature to the size of the body and the heat-emitting surface is of considerable importance. In very small warm-blooded animals, life in the polar regions is made more difficult by the fact that winter cooling cannot be adequately compensated for by metabolic heat. Thus the smallest arctic mammals that live in the open the whole time are arctic hares; lemmings, which are still smaller, take refuge from the extreme cold in burrows. Even in temperate regions it remains true that breeds living in cooler areas are usually bigger than those living in warmer areas (Bergmann's Law).

An important part in cooling the body is played by those parts of it which are hairless. It is no mere coincidence that these parts are often particularly extensive in tropical animals; one has only to think of the faces of apes, or of the skin of elephants and hippopotamuses. This lack of hair is almost completely absent in the mammals of colder lands. A similar effect is achieved by parts of the body such as legs, ears, and tails which never reach normal blood temperature at all. For this reason the only mammals suited to life in colder zones were those with the compact body and relatively short limbs,

---

The climbing ability of the ibex verges on the incredible. This stately wild goat, which is almost as strong as the red deer, finds no difficulty in negotiating cliffs and precipices that even the chamois cannot manage. (Photo: O. Färber.)

The rock gecko, a southern species of lizard. The gecko's 'sticky feet' work like suckers, so that the creature can walk on the smoothest and steepest rock faces. (Photo: L. Dorfmüller-Laubmann.) The eye is ideally adapted to the nocturnal habits of this lizard. Note the serrated rainbow skin (Photo: Dr Herbst/Antony.)

Too much grazing by cattle destroys the alpine pastures. 'Cattle walks' are a typical sign of danger. Here they cover the whole area of the slopes and provide surfaces for erosion to attack. (Photo: F. and E. Heimhuber.)

The alpine marmot, a kind of squirrel particularly well adapted to conditions in the mountains. (Photo: O. Färber.)

ears, and tails which distinguish the polar bear, arctic fox, and arctic hare.

Another means of regulating body temperature is modification of the body covering, which is a poor heat conductor. A good example is the thick coat of arctic mammals.

Obvious factors in heat husbandry are the links between temperature and colour of the body. Dark pigmentation assists the emission of heat and on the other hand warms the surface of the body by absorbing the sun's rays. Light colouring—that is, weak pigmentation—reduces the emission of heat from the body. That is why white

Foxes' ears provide an example of adaptation to external temperature (Allen's law). From left to right: arctic, red and desert fox.

animals are better suited to polar regions, where their colouring also serves as an ideal camouflage against enemies and beasts of prey. Or take the case of certain American predatory bugs, which have a black melanin pattern on a yellow or red background. The yellowish-red pigment (carotene) is situated in the epidermis of the larvae of the Colorado beetle. In a high temperature the carotene is oxidized and shed with the excreta; at the onset of cold it is stored in the top layer of skin. In the European cardinal beetle, which often appears on the trunks of old lime trees, the red pigment stored in individual patterns shows itself just as sensitive to changes of temperature: in unfavourable thermal conditions it is partly absorbed in the background colour.

Observation and experiment have also shown that the changes in colour of many lizards are influenced by changes in the temperature of their surroundings. For example, if the red-throated anolis, a native of the north-eastern parts of the U.S.A., is exposed to a temperature of only ten degrees centigrade, it takes on a brown colour. When the temperature goes up to twenty or thirty degrees, the anolis turns green; at forty degrees the colour changes to pale grey-green. In the same way the frilled lizard, the horned toad, and the spined lizard all display in low temperatures a dark colour which grows progressively lighter as the temperature rises. This change of colour is connected with the pigment cells in the animals' skins. These colour cells contain microscopically small grains of dark colouring matter: when these grains of pigment are spread evenly in the cells, the animal looks dark; but if they draw together in the centre of the cells the animal appears pale.

In the relation between temperature and the distribution of land animals an important part is also played by the relative size of the heart. A greater loss of heat over the surface of the body can be partly balanced by more intensive activity on the part of the heart. For this reason small animals tend on the whole to have a relatively larger heart than bigger animals with the same mode of life. The same is true of the warm-blooded animals of cool regions as opposed to related species from warmer lands.

So we see again and again that even warm-blooded animals can only overcome certain fluctuations in temperature if size of body and heart, the proportions of the exposed parts of the body, and the structure and colouring of the warming body covering are suitably developed, or if an adequate biochemical method of regulating heat is present.

As long as a living creature is not indissolubly bound to the ground beneath it, it will always strive to go where it can find the optimum satisfaction of its needs. This striving is clearly evident in the preference for certain temperature limits. For example, it is apparent in the case of certain insects and rodents that the species living in deserts and dunes prefer substantially higher temperatures than do those species occurring in marshy regions, deciduous forests, and alpine zones. The tuataras of New Zealand are most active in a temperature of only 12 degrees centigrade—by far the lowest temperature recorded for a reptile.

There are marked differences in the temperature favoured by ground insects according to whether they live on the surface or actually in the ground, and between species that live right inside a tree trunk and those to be found just under or on the bark; and again between organisms active in the summer and those which are active in the cool season. Unicellular organisms and threadworms in the cyst state, and likewise wheel animals (rotifera) and water-bears (tardigrades) in their resting state, can stand a temperature of minus 235 degrees centigrade in experiments, thus displaying a tolerance of cold paralleled only by bacteria, diatoms, and plant seeds and spores.

Usually, however, the temperature range which allows an undisturbed rhythm of life ranges from a few degrees below zero up to about 50, or occasionally 60, degrees centigrade. Among the

58

exceptions which can stand greater extremes are arctic foxes and ptarmigans. They have been watched in the Arctic in a temperature of minus 35 centigrade, and in this extreme cold they were pursuing their normal activities. In spite of this very low external temperature the body temperature of the foxes was still over 39 degrees, and that of the ptarmigans 43 degrees—a difference of about 80 degrees! The microscopically small springtail *Hypogastrura* can remain alive between 40 degrees centigrade and minus 16 degrees centigrade.

First settlers on bare cliffs and weathered surfaces must endure extreme differences of temperature. Blue algae, and filamentous algae such as the orange-red, ink-stroke algae well known in the mountains, here unite in a living community, which is visible on rocks, though only if it is present in huge quantities, as a pale greenish patina of weathering. These lowly plants, which are very sensitive to heat, drought, cold, and wind, help to break up the surface of bare rocks and thus prepare the way for the formation of humus. They can stand a temperature of 60 degrees centigrade and almost as many degrees of frost. This is because they can store water in their gelatinous envelopes; there the water does not freeze and so cannot split the cell walls.

The connection between temperature and the development and growth of animals is unmistakable. A good example is the maturing period of eggs and sperms, which, in accordance with Van't Hoff's law, is halved when the average temperature rises ten degrees centigrade. Animals which lay eggs in every season, such as the corn-beetle, show particularly clearly the influence which an increase in temperature can exert on egg production. On the other hand, there are many instances where cold is just as important as a stimulus. This is shown by plant seedlings and insects' eggs, which freeze completely in winter but thaw out again in spring and continue their development quite unharmed. In fact, in many cases it has been shown that seedlings and eggs which have not been completely frozen produce stunted plants and weakly insects. The same seems to be true of many chrysalises, which only develop normally if they have been exposed to the cold of winter. Thus frost can be a germinating stimulus necessary for successful life and development.

In very dry summers many creatures that live in the ground go deeper, a phenomenon that can often be observed in wireworms and cockchafer grubs. Click-beetle grubs ('wireworms') usually go down only about a foot or 15 inches, but cockchafer grubs go to a depth of nearly three feet, where some moisture is usually retained. Similarly in wintry regions the creatures of the ground always seek out a particular micro-climate that suits them, either by entrusting themselves to the protection of the earth or by finding refuges under leaves, stones, and cushions of moss or in cracks and crevices. Others create a favourable climate for themselves and their brood by means of wax coverings, cocoons, coats of hair, and so forth. Ants open and shut the entrances to their nests on the sunny or shady side in accordance with their requirements, and in winter they either withdraw into special winter chambers or build proper winter nests.

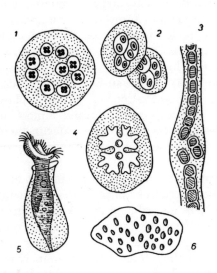

The Formation of Gelatinous Envelopes in Edaphic Organisms

1. *Spherical gelatinous bed of the* Gloeococcus (*green alga*).

2. *Gloeocystis (*green alga*) family of cells in bubble-shaped gelatinous envelope.*

3. *Gelatinous pipe of the* Ulothrix (*green alga*).

4. *Euastrum (*yoke alga*) in gelatinous coat.*

5. *Vaginicola (*infusorian*) in gelatinous beaker.*

6. *Aphanothece (*blue alga*) colony in a communal gelatinous envelope.*

PROTECTION AGAINST OVERHEATING

Warm-blooded animals protect themselves against excessive heat in their environment by seeking out shady, cool, and airy spots. Many marsupials, when suffering from the heat, lick the tips of their forelimbs; and if the need to shed heat grows stronger, they moisten large parts of their bodies with their tongues—obviously a means of creating artificial evaporation surfaces in the absence of sweat glands. When the physiological mechanisms set in motion by overheating do not function properly, animals exposed to extreme heat can die of heatstroke. Even cold-blooded animals can suffer heatstroke and death, as observations of reptiles show. Native species can stand a temperature of about 45 degrees for a limited period.

It was noted that small lizards of the Colorado desert in California died very quickly when they were exposed to the sun on sand with a temperature of over 57 degrees centigrade. Bigger desert lizards could stand such temperatures for 15 to 20 minutes, but died when their body temperature reached 47 degrees centigrade. During the cold desert nights they went stiff from the cold, and the next morning they had to be thoroughly 'warmed up' to normal living temperature before they showed any signs of life.

Lizards and snakes cannot regulate their body temperature by means of an internal safety mechanism; how then do they manage to avoid heatstroke in hot countries, especially deserts? Many species hide during the day in cool spots and in underground caves, only going out to look for food in the twilight and at night. Lizards, which eat during the day, only expose themselves to the hot sun for a short time, and they develop an exceptional nimbleness, so that they can move as quickly as possible across the sand and rock scorched by the rays of the desert sun. A few of them can change their dark colouring to a lighter one in the sun, and in this way can reflect some of the harmful heat rays.

These facts make the behaviour of the South American naked mole all the more surprising. Although its wrinkled body is completely naked, it goes on digging just under the surface of the ground even when the midday sun is blazing down; yet the air temperature is over 50 degrees and the sand is as hot as an oven. In this connection, Chinese butterfly lizards have an amazing need for heat. Their exceptionally flat bodies—when they are at rest they look almost disc-shaped—permit complete, double-sided 'irradiation', from above by the direct rays of the sun, and from below by reflected rays.

Not only snakes and lizards but also small mammals living under extreme desert conditions avoid excessive heating by appropriate behaviour. Many nocturnal animals spend the day in deep clefts and caves, where the temperature is moderate and constant, and where there is also a certain amount of moisture. Many small rodents, such as jerboas, also stop up the entrances to their underground homes with earth.

Ants react to the threat of overheating in midsummer by adding to their nests numerous additional openings and deeper shafts, which make better ventilation possible. Rainy weather provokes increased building activity.

According to the latest investigations it is believed that a satisfactory explanation has also been found for the occurrence of regular 'fungus gardens' in the nests of termites. The original assumption that the carefully tended networks of fungus served exclusively as food is now questioned. On the occasion of an expedition to East Africa by the Swiss Tropical Institute a termite colony of about 2000 insects was placed in an artificial nest and watched for two months. During this time the inhabitants looked after the development and enlargement of a fungus garden that had been provided for them. Their behaviour led to the conclusion that the mycelium is only seldom devoured. It may be that it serves as a source of vitamins, but the main purpose of the fungus garden seems to lie in another domain. As a result of fermentation and the activity of bacteria, temperature and moisture content in the fungus are higher than they are in the rest of the nest. They are affected very little by external influences and are of decisive importance in establishing the temperature and moisture-content of the nest as a whole. It would thus seem that the 'fungus garden' is to be regarded as a piece of biological equipment for the control of the climate.

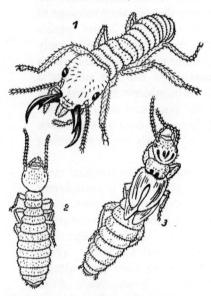

Wasps obtain the warmth necessary for their young in part direct from the sun's rays and in part through the heating of the air by the sun. If the temperature rises too high, they cool the nest by using their wings as fans. The larvae of certain diptera or two-winged insects have been found still

Reticulitermes, *termite (North America).*
1. *Soldier.* 2. *Fully grown worker.* 3. *Nymph (Last stage).*

alive at 55 degrees centigrade. However, in general it is fair to say that insects that live in the ground are very sensitive to overheating and that even temperatures well below the coagulation point of protein (65 degrees centigrade) are sufficient to injure them severely. Only a few organisms can go on existing in extremely high temperatures. The spores of sewage and refuse bacteria are not destroyed even when they are heated up to 60 or 70 degrees centigrade. Some fungi sprout and grow only in a temperature of some 55 degrees.

LIFE AMID ICE AND SNOW

Resistance to cold depends largely on the season, and on the physiological condition, sex, and stage of development of the animal concerned; it is closely bound up with the total water and fat content of an organism. The smaller the content of free water, the lower the freezing point. What low temperatures can be tolerated by plants and creatures of the soil is shown by the inhabitants of arctic and sub-arctic regions.

The vegetation of such regions consists mainly of shallow-rooted growths which procure at least a fraction of the organic substances they need from their own dead stalks and leaves. A dwarf larkspur has been found growing 19,000 feet up in the Himalayas. In Northern Siberia there is a scurvy-grass which blooms during the onset of the polar winter with its 50 degrees of frost; it spends nine months frozen stiff and then continues its interrupted blooming as soon as the short summer season has melted away the snow. All this indescribably meagre plant life utilizes literally every ounce of humus in the cracks in the ground, into which the roots sink greedily.

In the cold soil of the tundra plants suffer from lack of nitrogen, for in the low temperatures prevailing their roots can absorb but little water and therefore only small quantities of nutritive salts. Basically they display three different types of root system. First there are the species whose roots penetrate into the icy soil itself; then those which grow with their roots in the sub-soil and almost reach the permanently frozen strata; and finally the polar willows, dwarf birches, and dwarf bushes, which are rooted in the layer of humus which is partly matted with mycorrhiza-forming fungi.

Extreme resistance to cold is shown by the lowly snow vegetation, which always arouses attention through the striking colouration of the snow. Thorough investigations have shown that even in the monotonous-looking expanses of eternal snow there can be important differences between one spot and another. The presence *en masse* of *Chlamydomonas* is the most frequent reason for the red colour of the snow, both in the polar regions and in the mountains of Europe, but it is not the only one. There is often snow in Norway and the South American Andes which is coloured pink by other varieties of algae.

Red snow is indubitably the most common example of colouration by micro-plants, but one also finds yellow, brown, green, and even black snow. Yellow snow seems to occur more frequently in the Antarctic; it is caused by two species of green algae. In the Tatra Mountains in Czechoslovakia, algae (*Ankistrodesmus*) cover the

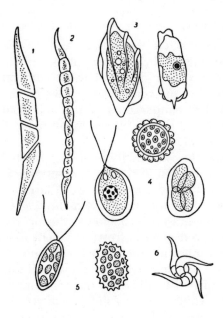

Plants growing on Ice and Snow
(*Cryophytes*)

  1. Rhaphidonema chodati
(*green alga*).
  2. Rhaphidonema sabaudum
(*green alga*).
  3. Scotiella nivalis (*Flagellate*).
  4. Chlamydomonas nivalis
(*Flagellate*).
  5. Chlamydomonas alpina
(*Flagellate*).
  6. Gyorffyella tatrica
(*green alga*).

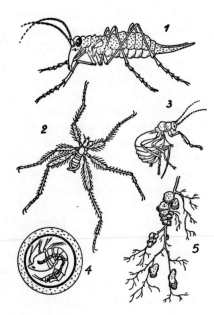

Tiny Animals which Live through the
Winter. They are Distinguished by
their Great Resistance to Cold.

  1. *Winter-fly* (Boreus hiemalis),
*which belongs to the order of scorpion-
flies.*
  2. Chionea araneoides, *a spider-
like, wingless gnat.*
  3. *Gall-nut wasp* (Biorhiza ap-
tera), *female of the winter generation.*
  4. Canthocamptus—*web-footed
crab in its winter cyst.*
  5. *Root-galls caused by* Biorhiza.

snow with a bright emerald carpet. Black patches in the snow, which occur principally in the Carpathians and the Engadine, usually owe their origin to a certain mixture of algae.

None of these algae is an accidental inhabitant of the snow, blown there from the ocean and enabled to increase by lack of competition. On the contrary, they are all special snow varieties, which only occur here and must have developed marked physiological peculiarities. It must be admitted that we still know very little about these peculiarities, for all attempts to cultivate these algae have so far been unsuccessful.

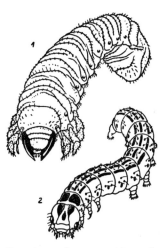

In the indescribably hard and hostile conditions above 19,000 feet—in the Himalayas, for example—primitive animals are found as well as a few kinds of diatoms. A curiously shaped species of water-bear has been discovered at a height of more than 22,000 feet and occasionally in the Antarctic, too, under fifteen feet of ice!

Numerous insects and spiders are distinguished by exceptional resistance to cold, especially some varieties of springtail, such as the glacier flea and certain snow fleas, which quite often appear on snow and glacier ice in such quantities that here and there they give the gleaming snow a dark tinge, rather like fine soot.

Insect larvae that are sensitive to the cold. 1. Cockchafer grub (Melolontha). 2. Caterpillar of the root-moth (Agrotis vestigialis).

Insects as a whole stand up well to very low temperatures. They often freeze as hard as stone in their winter hideouts, then thaw out in the first strong rays of the spring sun and emerge from their crevices in the ground. The nunataks of Greenland and the Antarctic continent—isolated peaks projecting like islands from the snow and ice—have their own characteristic, cold-resistant fauna, mainly various species of mites and daddy-long-legs, isopods, and insect larvae, which are so insensitive to low temperatures that they freeze up in cracks and crevices, then thaw out and resume their activities in the lichens and mosses quite unharmed.

Cold becomes the really essential limiting factor in the tundra, with its endless fields of snow and ice, its bare rocky slopes by the shores of the Arctic Ocean, where only lichens and mosses can grow, and its moors, marshes, and bogs. Conditions of life in this region, which stretches in a huge belt across the northern parts of America and Eurasia, are by nature bleak and hard, and the fauna correspondingly limited, though by no means poor in species.

From a nutritional point of view, animals and plants are linked together in manifold ways and forced to depend on each other; this is true of reindeer, arctic foxes, and lemmings, of voles and bog-ants, and of predatory beetles and spiders. Simple organisms such as mites and midge larvae are important links in the food chain between vegetation and the big animals; they find favourable feeding conditions in the neighbourhood of the lemmings' nests and runs. In the spring, when the snow is melting, the newly hatched midge larvae find plenty of rotted vegetable matter and unicellular creatures to feed on in the puddles. As the eggs of the myriads of midges only mature when the midges have sucked blood, the females depend in turn on the rodents, which are present in huge quantities in the form of lemmings and voles. The small rodents also form the main food of the predatory mammals, wolves, arctic foxes, wolverines, and ermines. Every fluctuation in the population has repercussions on the whole structure of life, whether the fluctuation occurs among the rodents (lemmings) or in the world of mites and simple insects.

The special conditions of the tundra force animals to conform strictly to the course of the year. The frozen state of the ground prevents animals from burrowing into it, while on the other hand the summer is very short for the collection of winter supplies. As a result, none of the animals in the tundra sleeps through the winter. The thick blanket of snow preserves all the plant life; lemmings and voles burrow under the snow for roots, and partridges look in the same way for berries, buds, and leaves. The abundant supply of food in the summer makes possible the formation of a thick layer of fat; but in any case the genuine tundra mammals are protected against the cold by thick furry coats.

Reindeer roam about in the taiga, where the herds break up and live in scattered groups, which unite again in the spring. Insects fall into a state of suspended animation in the autumn and can stand outside temperatures as low as minus 50 degrees, for under the blanket of snow a milder micro-climate prevails. Insects enjoy hardly three months of active life in the whole year, and many of them need two, and sometimes even three, summers to complete one single generation because the cumulative amount of warmth

66

they require to develop is simply not reached in one year on the tundra. On the other hand, simple insects, which develop relatively quickly, are quite numerous.

Exceptional sensitivity to cold is displayed by cockchafer grubs, which cannot stand more than minus 4 degrees centigrade; the same is true of grasshoppers and ants. The red forest ant dies of cold after a short stay in surroundings 1½ degrees below zero. It has been observed in Russia that the mosquito (*Anopheles*) can live through the winter in places where average temperatures of minus 18 degrees centigrade prevail for months on end.

Most of the creatures that live permanently in the ground usually avoid daily and seasonal fluctuations in temperature by going deeper. Earthworms and cockchafer grubs spend the winter in deeper, frost-free strata; isopods too withdraw from the upper strata in winter. In frost the mole goes deep, where he will find his principal food, earthworms and grubs.

4 *Water—Basic Element of Life*

PLANTS GROPE FOR WATER

There is no life on earth without water; even the soil can only support life when water flows through it, if only through the finest capillaries. The development of the soil and humus is dependent on water; water is indispensable to all soil processes. The water in the earth not only maintains the colloidal, watery, gelatine structure so important for the composition of the soil; it also has an extensive influence on the growth of plants and thus on the balance of vegetation.

In all organisms water is the factor with the greatest importance for all the processes of life. Protoplasm functions only when it is by water; if it dries up, it either perishes or passes into an inactive condition in which it stays until it can absorb water again. The importance of water to plants becomes clear when we realize that to produce one single gram of wheat—about 25 grains—roughly 23 cubic centimetres of water are required.

The higher the water content is, the more intensive—within certain limits—the manifestations of life. For example, young, quick-growing, swiftly reacting seedlings can be up to 90 per cent water; on the other hand, old, dead, woody cells are only about 50 per cent water. In dry grains of wheat the water content is about 13 per cent; during germination it climbs rapidly and when the wheat is ripe it reaches over 75 per cent, then sinks to 15 per cent in the dead straw.

Water is no problem to those simpler plants which are continually washed by it in the waters inside the soil. In many plants adapted to more or less lengthy periods of drought, special spongy tissues allow quick absorption (but slow loss) of water, so that the dormant periods are made as short as possible. In addition, the possession of spongy tissue, which is particularly characteristic of lichens and mosses, also permits the absorption of water vapour from the air. In damp mountain forests the ground is often covered with a particularly luxuriant growth of moss and lichen because of this adaptation to water vapour. The seeds of most of the higher plants obtain water through their husks, which are absorbent. The seeds of the golden rod and the poppy, as well as those of most varieties of wheat, germinate by absorbing water vapour if the humidity is not less than 98 per cent.

The roots anchor the plant to the ground, and through them the underground absorption of water takes place. Some trees, such as the pine, have shallow, spreading roots. Others send their roots deep down into the soil until they reach the subterranean streams of ground water. In their search for moisture roots avoid every obstacle. This sensitive hydrotropism goes so far that the roots of alders and willows can be 'attracted' into drainage and water pipes. In these special conditions they produce a wealth of long growths and develop into tangles of roots like horses' tails—they are sometimes called 'pigtails'—and in the end can block the pipes completely. Mangrove plants growing in coastal swamps in the tropics, where the mud is deficient in oxygen, develop long roots like stilts, which fulfil the function of air roots, absorbing the necessary oxygen from the air. The achievement of a plant's root, which penetrates the soil with an absorptive system of almost unimaginable surface area, can only be regarded as amazing. It has been established that the roots of one single wheat plant—including all the little hairs on the roots—can attain a total length of more than 70,000 yards!

The development of vegetation on the earth is best understood as essentially a result of the activity of water and light. If we compare plant life in the water and plant life on land, we can see that the simplicity of the former is the consequence of the incomparably more favourable conditions prevailing in the water. On land, on the other hand, the very struggle for water may have been the impulse to further development and refinement, which have finally led to the present variety of land vegetation, a variety whose mere outward appearance is enough to show that a harmonious balance has been struck between intake and emission of water.

The amount of water available to plants in each individual climatic region of the earth differs so widely that one is tempted to regard the vegetation of any particular landscape as simply a function of the available water. The damp tropics are characterized by the lush vegetation of the rain forests, and the sub-tropical regions by arid deserts and the transitional forms of plant life found in dry forests and steppes. In the temperate zones we find moisture-loving deciduous forests and hardy conifers.

The great importance of water to the life of a plant is immediately obvious from the difference in appearance between plants that grow in dry regions and those belonging to moister environments. The former frequently possess a small transpiratory surface, which in addition is usually protected against too great loss of water by a coating of hair or wax. 'Hygromorphic' plants, on the other hand, are distinguished by tender foliage, whose large surface area makes it quite clear that these plants can give off large, if not unlimited, quantities of water.

It is true that the relations between a plant's water economy and its shape are not always so simple and clear, as we can see from the example of the robinia, which grows in dry places. Its hygromorphic leaves seem at first to be a contradiction, but this is soon resolved when we realize that the robinia has a particularly well-developed root system, which enables it to absorb sufficient moisture even from the driest soil. Similarly, plants from extremely dry areas, such as cactuses, quite often thrive in very wet soil; but in these cases the ground water is usually so salty that plants find it difficult to absorb, so that to them the soil is for all practical purposes 'dry'.

Fundamentally it is true to say that the presence or absence of a plant in any particular area is due not so much to the turnover of water in favourable conditions as to the existence—or lack—of regulating mechanisms which can come into play to preserve life when water supplies are poor. Thus one of the most reliable indications of moist or dry mode of life is resistance to drought—the capacity to withstand loss of water. Plants from damp places usually die if they lose twenty per cent of their water, while genuine 'dry' plants can temporarily part with half their water without suffering damage.

FOREST AND STEPPE

Hardly any other plant community plays such a dominating and decisive role in nature's water cycle as the forest. The forest has its own special climate, which consists of a mosaic of micro-climates, and influences the climate as a whole. The forest filters the water in

70

the form of drops from drifting fog, it reduces the number of extreme climatic phenomena and has the same levelling effect in individual instances. As a natural result, extensive clearings where all the trees have been felled make themselves felt with unfavourable consequences, especially in dry years. They cause a lowering of the water-table, which in turn leaves the topsoil washed out and dry; 'steppification' sets in. Forests keep the soil porous, increase its capacity to absorb water, and, especially in the mountains, work as sponges, for they suck up the heavy downpours of rain and prevent the water from running away uselessly, carrying all the fine soil with it and leaving behind a bare skeleton.

Uncontrolled felling, which has reached alarming proportions in many parts of the world, leads to loss of water, destruction of humus, and soil erosion. For example, in the western parts of the United States forest after forest was felled over a period of many years, in order to turn wood and wheat into dollars. The bitter consequences soon made themselves felt; people had failed to realize that when forests disappear the rain disappears too. The cornland dried out and was eroded by the wind; hundreds of thousands of square miles of the best arable land were ruined. Reports on erosion and 'steppification' are continually appearing, but in spite of this forests are still being felled at an alarming speed in every continent: on the Amazon, in Canada, where the lumberjack is cutting deeper and deeper into the glorious forests of fir and pine, and in Australia, where there is talk of felling the rich tropical forests on the Great Barrier Reef. Metternich once made this pronouncement, which is unfortunately only too true: "Civilization and uncontrolled exploitation of the soil usually go hand in hand; the first deserts came into existence where the oldest civilized peoples lived, and fresh deserts have been produced wherever the civilized world has lost its reverence for the laws of nature."

Because of their wide distribution on every kind of ground—from rocks to forest and moorland—and their sponge-like nature, which enables them to absorb considerable quantities of water, mosses are in general of great importance in the ground's water economy. The sponge effect of mossy turf is usually substantial.

The stems and leaves of the most important mosses are built up out of two kinds of cells. Besides the chlorophyll-holding cells, there are cytoplasm-free cell spores, which act as water reservoirs; they are usually stiffened by fibrous strands, and communicate with each other and with their surroundings through round openings. Like the arrangement of the leaves, the capacity to absorb water varies from one species of moss to another: it can amount to nineteen times the plant's own weight.

Grasses are better adapted than almost any other kind of plant to low and irregular rainfall. These adaptations begin under the surface; the roots of the grasses are so deep and thickly intertwined that scarcely any other plant can gain a foothold. Above ground, the leaves display a number of different adaptations to aridity; blankets of hair, coatings of wax, and, in the same cases, the ability

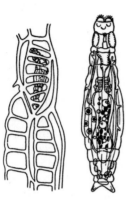

Water-holding cells of sphagnum moss with the wheel animal Callidina reclusa *living in them. To the right, a more highly magnified sketch of the tiny symbiont.*

to curl up, ensure that the leaves can soon stop giving off water as soon as the ground ceases to deliver sufficient moisture. It is true that all these arrangements lose their effectiveness in a genuine drought—the blades wither and lend the landscape of the steppe a comfortless, almost hostile look. Only when the first rain falls does the grassland grow green again.

The tropical rain forest exhibits many interesting features. The huge trunks of the trees stand in the ground like pillars; their roots are the most curious to be found in the plant kingdom—stilt roots many yards high and fantastic flat roots like planks. The younger trees are completely overgrown by other plants, so much so that they

An underground burrower emerges into the light of day: the mole with his huge hands like shovels. (Photo: L. Dorfmüller-Laubmann.)—A relic of long past ages, the armadillo is one of the most remarkable of the mammals. Its home is South America, where such curious creatures as the sloth and the ant-eater also live. Huge claws make the armadillo a skilful digger. (Photo: P. Popper.)

(Overleaf) The elephant forces his way through the bush with destructive power. (Photo: Dr A. Lindgens.)

The dormouse spends more than half the year in its winter sleep. (Photo: A. Niestle/Bavaria.)

Its prickly coat protects the hedgehog from many enemies when it curls up. (Photo: B. Schuhmacher.)

are unrecognizable. On the forks of the branches bushes of fern flourish, like huge stork nests. The smaller branches are covered with tightly compressed bunches of orchids—a sea of fragrant, brightly coloured blossoms! But beauty is accompanied by terror—curtains of prickly lianas, more spiteful than a barbed wire entanglement. In the midst of all this more plants are growing on the others like nests, so that there are collections of humus even in the upper layers of vegetation. This 'hanging soil' supports the same communities of animals as the floor of the forest. Since there are no serious daily

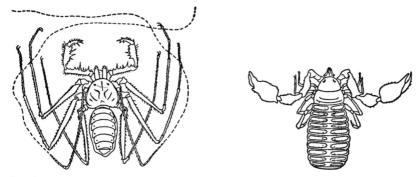

Scorpions: on the left, the whip-scorpion Charinus *from Africa (after Millot, modified); on the right, the pseudo-scorpion* Chelifer cyrneus, *a genuine bark-dweller.*

fluctuations in air temperature at ground level either, the herbaceous vegetation which flourishes in the shade of the tree tops lives in an atmosphere of uniform moisture. When, however, downpours of rain have fallen on the tropical forest, the air is transformed into a hot, damp, steaming vapour. It causes the decomposition of every-thing organic on the ground with incredible speed. The plant roots immediately absorb the nutriment which is freed by the process of disintegration and the rest sinks into the ground. Thus the whole nutritional capital of the virgin forest's soil lies in the vegetation.

The high moisture content of the air in those layers of the forest close to the ground forces the plants there to adopt various different arrangements to facilitate transpiration. While the plants growing 100 or 150 feet up catch the rainwater with air roots and store it in bulges in their stems, the plants below on the forest floor develop waterproof leaves, so that the rainwater quickly runs off them. Very often the ends of the leaves are also drawn out in long points, which act as gutters and help the water to run off. The decisive ecological factor in the tropical rain forest is thus moisture.

Moreover, it was deep forests that were first inhabited by land animals in primitive times, so it is not surprising that the fauna of the rain forests show many very ancient characteristics. We have only to think of the Indo-Malayan tupaja, a primitive intermediate form on the boundary between insectivores and primates, of skinks, tapirs, and the curious okapi, of slow-worms, of cylindrical snakes, termites, scorpions, millipedes, and many other creatures—all representatives of earlier, original groups of animals. Furthermore, the moisture-saturated air of the tropical rain forests encouraged the development of moisture-loving creatures which are only poorly represented, if at all, in the forests of our temperate latitudes. Hence the great variety of worms and snails; even true water-creatures, such as crabs and fish, take to the coastal forests; many toads and wood frogs spawn in holes in the ground instead of in the water; and marine bristleworms and sand-fleas can live on the land when the air is saturated with moisture. Not only does the impenetrability of the bush impede animals' sight; the prevailing calmness of the air also makes it difficult for them to get their bearings by means of the sense of smell.

There is also abundant life in the forest soil, which—thanks to the swift disintegration of organic matter—has only a thin covering of litter. In the rain forest, too, soil life is most thickly concentrated in the top four inches and decreases quickly further down. Rotting tree trunks form the foundation of life for many organisms, particularly those that eat wood, humus, and fungi. The surface of the ground is dominated by ants, and it is significant that the creatures that live on the ground in temperate latitudes inhabit the upper layers of vegetation in the tropical rain forests. Evidence of this is provided by the tree-nests of termites, frogs, and a number of mammals which originally lived on the ground. Nor are there many species of birds that live on the ground.

A special kind of rain forest is found on the flat, surfless tropical coasts, particularly on the banks of the often intricate deltas of the bigger rivers. Here, in the tidal zone, we find formations known as mangrove or gallery forests. The trees are anchored in the mud by great arching stilt roots which often span a circle ten yards in diameter, and can thus successfully resist the pull of the tides. Frequently shapes like knees or sugar loaves come to the surface from the thick tangle of roots; they are air roots, which have to take over the essential task of breathing, for which the thick muddy soil provides little opportunity, especially as it is covered every day by the tides.

Other noteworthy peculiarities of genuine mangrove plants are long-lasting fruits that can float, and the fact that the seedlings cling for a long time to the mother plant, so that when they fall off they can more easily gain a footing in the mud before they have a chance to be carried away by the tide. The network of roots and branches traps the muddy sediment of floating particles of soil. Thus mangroves contribute to the building up of fresh land.

PLANT LIFE UNDER A PARCHING SUN

Just as forest turns into tree-dotted savannah and then into grassland as soon as the rainfall falls off, so steppe and grassland turn into desert as the shortage of water becomes more acute. Here lack of water plays the predominant rôle; all other ecological factors retire into the background. The bizarre variety of desert vegetation itself provides evidence of the ways in which plants have adapted themselves to the lack of water in their environment.

First of all, there are numerous desert plants which betray no adaptations to drought at all; these are the rain plants, with their thin, tender stalks. They do not struggle for water; their method consists in severely curtailing the period of growth and confining it to the rainy season. They spend the dry season in the ground as tubers, bulbs, or seeds. But in really dry regions such plants form a very small minority. The majority possess devices for reducing, either permanently or temporarily, the amount of water they give off, and they usually develop very long roots. Very often the devices that limit transpiration lie in the anatomical construction of desert plants: thickening and compression of the outer walls or the formation of layers of wax, resin, or lime on the epidermis. The epidermis of many plants of the desert and steppe can be so thick and so well provided with storage facilities that these plants can hold water for years. Further adaptations are the covering of the epidermis cells with slime, the narrowing or caulking with resin or wax of the stomata (openings in the leaves), and the sinking or arching-over of the stomata in depressions in the epidermis.

Very often anatomical modifications of this sort are linked to peculiarities in the external structure which likewise reduce evaporation. Thus many desert plants have developed a thick coating of hairs of one sort or another, which fill with air and lend the plant a white or grey colouring. Another device to guard against evaporation is the vertical positioning of the blades, either by turning them or by the laminated formation of the leaf stalks, as in the case of the

Australian acacia. When the sun is at its highest point in the heavens
—that is, at the hottest time of the day—most of its rays pass on
either side of leaves like these.

The need to husband water causes other plants that grow in rain-
less deserts to reduce their transpiring surface sharply—in relation
to their extensive root systems—either through dwarfing of the whole
plant or through stunting or modification of the leaves. Desert
plants mostly have very small leaves; hence the parched, thirsty
appearance of desert and steppe vegetation.

This world of parched vegetation begins on the limestone rocks
round the Mediterranean, in Corsica, for example, and Dalmatia;
it is rich in thorns and prickles, with their shining, leathery leaves
which look as if they have been cut out of tin and then lacquered. In
the Arabian and Persian deserts, and under the blazing sun of Africa,
plants shed almost all their leaves, so that not a drop of precious
moisture is wasted. In these places, where often there is scarcely
any rain for years and plants have to make do with dew, they turn
into a mass of pointed thorns, with tiny leaves or even none at all,
so that stem and branches have to take over the task of assimilating
nourishment. The frightful thorn hedges of the Alhazi and the
tragacanth bushes and leafless forests of prickly pear trees in the
heart of Asia stretch for mile after mile. Nevertheless, Sven Hedin
writes that such a forest seemed to him like a Garden of Eden after
he had walked for days through the vast, terrible *kewir*, the Persian
salt desert, which frequently offers the eye literally nothing but an
empty, glittering sky and a blinding, white expanse of salt. The
desert plants known as succulents fill a special tissue with water
during the short rainy periods and store it up for the long periods of
drought. Organs in which this tissue is highly developed become
very thick, fleshy, and juicy. In many succulents of the desert and
steppe the roots have been thickened and developed into storage
spaces for water; these are the root succulents, such as certain
umbellate plants, composites and gourds. More common are the
leaf succulents, such as the agave and other species known as 'living
pebbles', which adapt themselves perfectly in form and colour to the
surrounding desert rock and provide a good example of 'plant
mimicry'. But undoubtedly the most widely distributed and best
known are the stem succulents: the spherical, barrel-shaped, and
pillar-shaped cacti of the New World and the pillar- or candlestick-
shaped *Euphorbia* and the cactus-like *Asclepiadaceae* of the Old
World.

76

The quality of succulence is a frequently recurring phenomenon which shows how in similar surroundings the same ecological adaptation to climatic peculiarities has been developed in quite different, widely removed families. Among the leaf succulents, the African aloe has a baffling resemblance to the American agaves, while under the influence of the African desert climate the spurge family has produced forms which can hardly be distinguished from the cacti of American dry regions. The cactus form does in fact provide the smallest possible surface area in relation to the size of the plant, and therefore transpires least. For example, a spherical cactus has a surface area three hundred times smaller than a leafy twig of the same weight from a climbing plant, and loses five hundred times less water by evaporation in any given period of time.

The Arctic is another region with a low rainfall and polar vegetation has to withstand summer droughts. Those specialists in dryness, the mosses and lichens, give the northern tundra such a characteristic stamp that we are fully entitled to speak of moss and lichen tundras. Just as the lichens are the first plants to appear on the bare rocks of the Alps, so they are also among those which have advanced farthest towards the pole. The temporary periods of complete drought hold no dangers for them, since they are in a position, with the help of their spongy tissue, to absorb water from the damp and frequently misty air. The dry climate compels the other plants of the tundra to take just the same precautions against evaporation as desert plants do: they are low and compact, the roots spread out not far below the surface, and the leaves are small and tough. Many of them reproduce through runners as well as seeds, and even if their growth is slow it takes only a few weeks of polar spring to set them in full bloom.

ANIMALS AND WATER

The proportion of water in terrestrial animals fluctuates within fairly wide limits. Sixty per cent of the adult human body is water, a third in the blood and the other body fluids, the remainder distributed among the cells of the body. During the period of active life mammals contain between 60 and 70 per cent water, an edible snail about 85 per cent, and earthworms up to 88 per cent. The proportion of water in insects varies from about 45 per cent in fully developed adults with hard chitin armour to 92 per cent in soft-skinned larvae. Dormant chrysalises and hibernating forms have—independently of the amount of body fat present—less water than active, growing larvae. This is shown clearly by the example of leaf beetles: the larva is about 80 per cent water, the chrysalis hardly 75 per cent, and the fully developed insect with its powerful armour scarcely 66 per cent. If the water content sinks below a certain level, which naturally varies from species to species and according to stage of development, the creature perishes. In the case of the larva of the Colorado beetle, for example, this level is about 60 per cent; with termites it is higher—roughly 68 per cent.

Water can enter the body in very different ways. It can be drunk, taken together with food (perhaps chemically compounded with it),

Potato or Colorado beetle (Leptino-tarsa decemlineata), *one of the most feared agricultural pests. On the left, the larva.*

or absorbed through the surface of the body. In the driest steppe and desert regions there are some animals which can make do with very little water indeed. This is true of many antelopes and gazelles and also of the ground squirrel and other rodents. Camels can go without water for many days and numerous reptiles drink but seldom. Herbivorous animals are content with the liquid they obtain from tubers and bulbs or from the tissue of succulents. Some weevils and beetles like to nibble the heads of certain species of thistle which bloom at the time when water is in shortest supply. The juice that flows from wounds inflicted by this process is drunk greedily by bees, wasps and ants. Some Peruvian species of cactus are inhabited by the larvae of hover-flies and other insects, which find enough liquid there to satisfy them. For many arthropods, for many snails, and even for some mammals the dew is an adequate source of water. Many animals, especially hoofed ones, drink salt water because they need the minerals. Water in solid form, particularly snow, is quite acceptable.

When animals drink, they can do it in very different ways. Mammals drink through the lips with the help of the tongue; a good example is the dog. Badgers and racoons drink by means of a mixture of scooping and masticating; the lower jaw is thrust down into the liquid and scoops it up. Elephants and gibbons drink by indirect methods: the elephant uses its trunk and the gibbon hangs over the water by its hinder end and scoops it up with its free hand. There are a few land mammals that do not drink. No one has yet observed a sloth drinking in its natural surroundings. The koala bear—prototype of the teddy bear—does not drink either; hence its name, for 'koala' means 'does not drink' in the language of the aborigines. Koalas have been known to drink in captivity, but only when they were ill.

Some natives of the desert and steppe live on food dried in the air, and utilize the liquid released in the oxidation of the food—the metabolic water. This can be demonstrated quite clearly in the case of the jumping mice of the Arizona desert, which eat only dry seeds.

Some animals absorb water through the skin, but this is only possible when the air is relatively moist. Amphibians and snails 'drink' through their skins; so do centipedes and ticks. Insect larvae, too, can absorb water through the skin from both damp substances and moist atmospheres. In the driest periods the jumping mice already mentioned withdraw into their underground burrows— sometimes three feet deep—where the air is moister; here the mere breathing of the damp air brings a sufficient gain in moisture. The absorption of water from the air is not simply a process of diffusion, that is, a physical process; it probably depends also on the active contribution of the cells of the body, on an internal 'water secretion' based on hygroscopic qualities in the skin.

Of course, many desert animals certainly do need water. They are capable, as we know from numerous mammals and amphibians, of steering straight for sources of moisture, and often cover consider-able distances in order to find water for themselves and their young. Animals often walk for hours to water holes, and it is amazing to see what a highly developed instinct they have for finding their way to water in the steppe or desert. Insects, too, frequently make purposely for certain areas of moisture. In springtails and earwigs the sense for moisture is localized in the feelers. It is well known that desert frogs make full use of any rain, regardless of the season; some species lay their eggs in the sand, covered in a mass of foam, and the embryos develop so much that they can emerge as soon as any rain falls.

In the case of land animals, there are also unmistakable connec-tions between the body and the water content of the food. Insects

79

which live on damp food contain relatively more liquid in their bodies than those which eat only dry food.

All land animals lose a certain amount of water through evaporation from the surface of the body, through breathing, or in defaecation and other excretion. They make extensive efforts to protect themselves against the danger of losing too much, which becomes more pressing as the external temperature rises. Animals have developed various kinds of protection against evaporation, according to whether they live in a dry or damp environment and according to the ease with which a deficiency of water can be made good. The protection may take the form of armour made of horn or chitin, or of hair and feathers.

During the dry season many desert animals dig themselves in. The desert toad, for example, digs holes over three feet deep and in winter makes tunnels over fifteen feet long.

It shares these burrows with black beetles, spiders, ticks, lizards, and mice. Desert insects, which include crickets, ants, earth bees, digging bees, and black beetles, are distinguished by an exceptional capacity for digging. The biological significance of this behaviour becomes particularly obvious in the case of desert ants, which, unlike the species which live in woodland, build crater nests with strikingly deep shafts, in which they can easily escape the dry heat. Snails, too, in really dry regions dig in during the winter, and it is known that Australian desert frogs retire into deep holes in the ground so as to reduce their loss of water to a minimum. In click beetles, many ground beetles, crickets, predatory bugs, and stick insects that live in the desert, as also in the above-mentioned black beetles, it has been noted that the wings have disappeared, and this, too, may help the conservation of water. In addition, in dry surroundings, quite a few land animals lose very little water in their excretions.

Nevertheless, it is impossible to avoid entirely the recurrent loss of body fluid, even if only for a short time, as in the case of the edible snail when it withdraws into its shell. In spite of their layers of chitin and the protection of the organs of secretion against loss of water, many insects can live only in damp surroundings. Certain primitive worms lose water by evaporation in dry air twice as quickly as earthworms and forty times as quickly as caterpillars. The water content of the tissue of many insect larvae amounts to 80 per cent; in unfavourable conditions they lose their moisture and perish. The drier the air is, the more quickly they die. On the other hand, some insects—locusts, for example—can maintain a water content of 70

Desert iguana from
tropical South America.

Zebra skink from Madagascar.
(Photos: L. Koch/Bavaria.)

per cent, even when the moisture in the air fluctuates between 30 and 80 per cent.

Evaporation through the surface of the body can be reduced in various ways: by horny armour, as in the case of reptiles, by firm shells with small openings, as in the case of snails, and by water-repellent or water-insulating layers of wax, as in the case of numerous arthropods. Evaporation is particularly well suppressed in bugs, beetles, and spiders, all of which possess such a layer of wax.

In breathing, loss of water can be avoided by temporary closing of the air-passage openings, as with desert insects.

Insects belonging to dry regions avoid losing water in metabolic excretions by sucking water back in the lower bowel. This occurs in the larvae of beetles and other insects which feed on very dry substances, in the ant-lion, with its very dry habitat, and in forms which may be compelled to go hungry for a long time in dry surroundings—for example, the oil-beetle larva.

Numerous land animals can live through long dry spells. For instance, many lizards remain rigid for long periods, and some mammals hibernate. Among the animals that do this are the aardvark of the African steppe, the rat-sized bristly hedgehog of Madagascar and the dainty little pouched dormouse of Australia, which often hibernates for long periods twice in the same year. In May bristly hedgehogs dig themselves deep burrows, into which they withdraw to hibernate during the dry southern winter. They do not appear on the surface again until December. Before this winter sleep they stuff themselves with food. The pouched mice do the same, storing up their supplies of fat in their tails. Some European mammals, too, which can live in southern regions, hibernate through dry periods; dormice and marmots, for example.

WATER AND HABITAT

Moisture is most constant in the hot, damp tropics, in caves, and other underground environments. Thus soft-skinned worms are only to be found in any real variety in the soil of the forest. The permanently moist soil of temperate and warm regions is always more thickly populated than dry soil, and it is only in this moist soil that we find numerous species of segmented worms and

Sand martins in front of their nesting holes. (Photo: E. Schuhmacher.)—That 'flying jewel', the gloriously coloured kingfisher, makes his nest in steeply sloping river banks, too. (Photo: P. Popper.)

thread-worms. Finally, caves and grottoes are inhabited by beetles and spiders with very soft, thin armour.

The maintenance of animal life on dry land necessitates special protective arrangements to guard against excessive evaporation of the body fluids. These arrangements may take the form of a hardening and thickening of the epidermis or of the shifting of permanently moist organs to the inside of the body. Thus the armoured arthropods, snails with their shells, and vertebrates with several layers of skin can inhabit the drier zones. The chitin covering of drought-resistant beetles is for the most part completely watertight, the epidermis of mammals is more or less horny, and the majority of the snails have a nocturnal mode of life and can live through long dry periods in a dormant condition with reduced metabolism. Just as decisive from a biological point of view is the fact that the permanently moist breathing organs and most of the organs with a chemical function are located in the interior of the body.

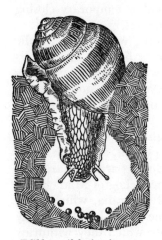

Edible snail laying its eggs.

There are several species of fish, too, which are endowed with the capacity to live an amphibious life. The best known of them are the snake fish, the biggest of which, the striped snake-head, lives in the marshes of the Indian lowlands. These fish survive the dry season by burying themselves in the mud. A relative of the snake fish, the Indian climbing fish, likewise obtains most of the oxygen it needs from the air, and this enables it to live for a time on dry land. When the pool in which it lives dries up, it retires into a narrow tunnel in the earth which it has dug for itself. In the mangrove swamps of tropical Africa and of Australia lives the curious mud skipper, a fish which can leave water for hours at a time and go hunting beetles and snails on dry land. It is enabled to do this by the narrow, chinky nature of the gill openings, which delays the evaporation of the water in the gill cavities. The fins on the belly have grown together and those on the breast, with which the mud skipper walks over the soft ground, are very long. When danger threatens, mud skippers hurry off as quickly as lizards and take refuge in the nearest water or dig themselves into the mud.

But there are certain fish which are still better adapted to breathing air because they possess lungs as well as the usual gills. One species of these amphibious fish is a native of Australia; others are the South American scaly newt and the newt fish of equatorial Africa. What makes them particularly interesting is the fact that their anatomy and mode of life give us valuable indications about the way in which the transition from water to land was probably made.

When in the hot season marsh and river bed go stagnant or dry out completely, making it impossible to breathe through gills, these living 'primeval fish', whose existence at an earlier period of the Earth's history can be proved, use their fins as feet and creep between the stones and clods of earth on to the land. There they dig themselves about eighteen inches into the ground, curl up with their tails over their heads, and then exude from the glands in their skin a tough slime which spreads over their bodies like a thin cocoon and thus saves them from drying up. A funnel over the mouth connects them with the outside world, so that they can breathe, and in this way they aestivate through the summer months in a state of suspended animation. If they are dug out carefully in their crust of mud and earth, they can be transported quite easily; the 'lumps of mud' come to life again as soon as they are put in lukewarm water. Like the hibernating mammals, these lungfish live during this curious summer 'sleep' on the fat which they have stored up in the rainy season.

In clay and loess deserts, there are interesting conditions where the surface of the ground is flat and hard. Here the rainwater does not penetrate far into the ground; for the most part it runs over the surface and naturally soon evaporates. However, the high capillarity of the tiny pores in the ground leads the deep-lying ground water up to the surface, so that shallow-rooted plants can thrive. As this moisture rises it brings up mineral salts with it, which crystallize very quickly. Reptiles, rodents, and birds are represented in these regions, mainly by lizards, hares, and desert fowl. Sandy deserts develop a surface dried by the air, under which the water is largely protected against evaporation. At a certain depth the upward movement of the water caused by capillary action and the downward movement of the rainwater strike a balance, which creates favourable conditions for deep-rooted plants.

The forms and distribution of plant and animal life on the steppes show many striking similarities with those of the desert. There are many plants that manage to survive with the help of underground organs, as succulents and thorn bushes do, but the main contingent consists of grasses and shrubs, whose roots often go down several yards. So far as the animal world is concerned, here too we find animals which seek protection from the hot days, cold nights, and violent storms by living in the ground: rodents in particular (pouched and crested rats, mole-rats, prairie dogs, ground squirrels, and hamsters) but also the fairy armadillo, the ant-eater, and the mole. Sand martins and bee-eaters nest in the walls of deep gullies eroded

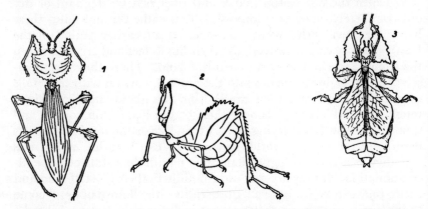

Tropical grasshoppers. 1. *African 'devil flower'* (Idolum diabolicum). 2. *East African* Plagiotriptus *grasshopper* (after Burr). 3. *'Walking leaf'* (Phyllium pulchrifolium) *from Indonesia. The creature's shape and colouration make it invisible among the leaves.*

by the rain; skinks, toads, and snakes burrow in the ground. Thanks to the nests they build, ants and termites are particularly well able to endure the climatic extremes of the steppes.

To turn to the animals that live above ground, two methods of movement are particularly characteristic of the steppes: running and jumping. The runners are represented by the giraffes, antelopes, hyaenas, jackals, cheetahs, ostriches, and bustards; the jumpers by the kangaroo, jumping hare, jumping mouse, grasshopper, and cicada. Unlike most of the inhabitants of the desert, the animals of the steppe are fairly gregarious. Horses, zebras, elephants, antelopes, and giraffes all live in herds, and the predators of the steppe—hyaenas, wolves, and lions—stalk their prey in packs. Even insects cling together, and it is well known that ants and termites form particularly populous colonies on the steppe.

Moisture conditions have produced areas and habitats comparable to steppe and desert in other climatic zones as well. We have only to think of rocky heathland, whose extremely dry and warm climate permits only a limited vegetation and range of animal life, or of rocky cliffs, which are no less extreme. Apart from sand martins, the main inhabitants of these spots are bees and wasps. The species comprising the various communities are determined not only by the steepness of the cliffs but also by the structure of the ground. Essentially, these spots are the home of diggers and climbers—grasshoppers, ants, and so on—but when the ground is softer scrapers

Examples of Anabiosis in Edaphic Organisms

1. *Encapsulated slipper animalcule* (Paramecium).

2. Bodo (*a flagellate*) *creeping out o*, *its cyst.*

3. *Protective capsule of* Euglena (*flagellate*).

4. Amoeba *in its cyst* (Amoeba terricola).

5. *Cyst of an infusorian from a pool* (Bursaria).

6/7. *Water-bears' eggs.*

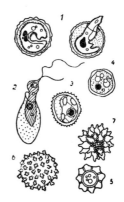

can make their dwellings there too. In the harder spots there are more creatures that dig with their mouths, particularly solitary wasps and bees. In the cracks and crevices in the rock spiders make their webs and the surface of the cliffs, which is often hot from the sunshine, is peopled by flies and shepherd spiders.

The plants and animals which live in shifting sand have to reckon with completely different conditions: large fluctuations in heat and moisture, the movement of the sand caused by the wind, and sparse vegetation consisting mainly of tough, perennial grasses. Many of the creatures that live in dunes adopt a strict daily rhythm and withdraw into the depths of the ground during the daytime. Toads dig themselves into the sand, and spiders take refuge from the heat and the movement of the sand in tunnels and webs close beneath the surface of the ground. It is noticeable that spiders, bugs, and beetles that live among dunes are long and narrow in shape; the narrow body enables them to hide between the blades of grass and thus offer the smallest possible area for the wind to attack.

Because of surface tension a certain proportion of the water contained in capillaries in the soil remains behind in the tiniest cavities; it takes the form of a thin film of water, which in turn can serve as a dwelling place for the smallest soil inhabitants. In any case the water in the ground is responsible for maintaining the watery, gelatinous structure necessary for the existence of the tiny edaphic organisms. These microscopic plants and animals need soil which is damp and crumbly and traversed by innumerable very fine 'veins' of water thinner even than a hair; the commonest of these organisms are flagellates, rhizopods, wheel animals, and thread-worms.

The organisms of the lower edaphon spend times of drought and the period when the ground is frozen in a state of rigidity with a reduced metabolic rate. They wrap themselves in a waterproof protective skin. This makes osmotic activity on the part of the cell impossible, for the outer membrane of the wall, now no longer smooth but rough and wrinkled, ceases to be permeable; it neither absorbs nor exudes any water. This condition of 'passive self-preservation' in a gelatine cyst is widespread in both plant and animal micro-organisms. A fairly thick layer of firm, gelatinous substance comes into being round the organism, which is usually compressed into the shape of a ball. In this phase the organism does not feed, hardly respires, and naturally does not reproduce.

The classic example of the edaphic organism that isolates itself from the outside world as soon as conditions become unfavourable is the water-bear or bear animalcule. Although zoologists with orderly minds have always found it difficult to classify them, these microscopically small creatures are real cosmopolitans. Their area of distribution is almost world-wide and reaches high up into the mountains. The terrestrial species are just as common in lichens and moss as in the damp, sandy banks of lakes and rivers; and just as much at home in Sumatra as in Spitzbergen and Kamchatka. They occur at a height of 10,000 feet in the banks of the mountain lakes of Titicaca in Peru, and isolated specimens have even been found over 20,000 feet up in the Himalayas. On the whole, moisture, light, and nature of the soil are more important in determining whether or not they are present than the species of plant which provides nourishment. When the cushions of moss dry up, these minute animals dry up, too; drawing in their heads, rear ends, and extremities, they assume the shape of a barrel. Experiments and observations showed that animals which had been in a dried-up condition for over six years came to life again when they were moistened. It was also proved that bear animalcules and their eggs (at any stage of development) are capable of drying up and coming to life again several times.

The notable number of cysts to be found in the ground in May in temperate regions of the Northern Hemisphere is attributable to the night frosts, to which the newly awoken edaphic organisms seem to be particularly sensitive; while the striking increase in the number of cysts in July and August leads to the conclusion that these creatures are still more sensitive to drought than they are to winter frosts. Most of the terrestrial algae, too, make use of these protective envelopes. Thread algae, which contribute a good deal to making

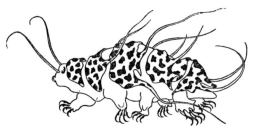

Even the world of everlasting ice is not without life. Echiniscus, *a curious representative of the bear animalcules from the glaciers of the Himalayas* (22,000 *feet*). *Real size, about* 0·5 *millimetre.*

the upper layers of soil mellow, encase themselves in thick, gelatinous tubes of slime; iron and ochre algae stitch themselves up with threads of slime.

Unquestionably the world of the lower edaphon is full of producers of organic colloids, and it is obviously here that we must seek the origin of the natural adhesives which play such an important rôle in the continual opening-up of the ground. All the slimy substances produced by the micro-organisms are excellently suited to retaining water, which is thus prevented from sinking down too quickly to join the ground water or from disappearing through evaporation.

An excess of moisture, too, can have an extremely unfavourable effect on many inhabitants of the soil. The thorough wetting of the earth which occurs when the snow melts forces many creatures in the ground to come up to the surface; this can be observed in the cases of springtails, carrion beetles, and short-winged insects.

87

WHERE LAND AND WATER MEET

Realms in which land and water come into close contact with each other have their own special character. Rivers and streams flow through the most varied kinds of landscape; springs, ponds, and lakes occur everywhere; and finally there are the sea coasts, with their mud, sand, rocks, and cliffs. In addition to these obvious border zones between land and water, there are the wide areas of the big rivers which flood, particularly round their deltas; here we find moisture-loving grasses, reeds, scrub, or extensive marshy forests. This kind of landscape is distinguished by water, wet soil, and often a moist atmosphere. It can offer extremely varied conditions of life. Examples are the papyrus marshes of the Nile, the swampy bamboo thickets of the tropics, and the reed forests of Europe and North America, which consist of reeds, red maces, and rushes.

The mechanical beat of the waves has left many stretches of bare shore along the edges of rivers, lakes, and seas; but in quieter bays, inland waters, and river mouths, as well as in the big flood areas, banks of reeds are formed whose plants root in the muddy bottom.

A middle stage between land and water fauna is represented by forms which live in the thin films of water which often cover stones, fragments of rock, leaves, and twigs in the neighbourhood of shallow streams. This typically amphibian fauna includes the larvae of caddis flies and thorn flies, and also some crane-fly larvae. On very calcareous soils we find the dainty butterfly-midge larva, the bristles on whose back and sides produce a deposit of lime in the form of thick crusts.

The creatures that move freely about the surface of mud flats display many characteristics that can be interpreted as adaptations to the surface on which they live. For example, the bodies of many mud-flat isopods are considerably flattened; the extremities are lengthened and kept spread out on each side, so that the creatures look rather like spiders.

The fauna that lives in the mud itself includes numerous tube-dwellers, for example the sandworm on the sea shore and the tube-worms (*Tubificidae*) on the banks of fresh water. Both play a rôle in the soil economy of the soft ground which generally attracts little attention but is in fact important—a rôle which resembles that of the earthworm in farmland. Thorough investigations lasting many years prove that on an average each worm moves four times its own weight, reckoned in dry material, every twenty-four hours. As a result of this constant sieving action slimy ground becomes porous and is increasingly mineralized. On mud flats in particular, diatoms play an important part in the formation of the soil. Billions and billions of these simple plants cover sandy flats, like a brownish-green carpet; with the gelatinous slime which they exude, they cement and mat together the topmost layer of mud.

A habitat of a rather special kind is the strips of sand above the waterline which often stretch out in long, low tongues from the banks of lakes and rivers and, more especially, the sea coast. On the coast, which is exposed to the ebb and flood of the tides, or at any rate to larger fluctuations in the height of the water, sea creatures predominate. Here, too, there are creatures that live in the ground, as there are in mud; they dig themselves in and construct extensive systems of tunnels or tubes in the sand. The tunnels of lugworms and sandhoppers (see p. 92) are generally passages with many branches; their walls consist of grains of sand cemented together with a secretion. A genuine native of damp sand is the sand-flea, which can be seen hopping about on mud flats at low tide. This creature does not live in the water, but exclusively in the damp sand of the sea shore; it avoids both water and dry ground.

Unlike soft liquid mud, damp sandy ground offers possibilities for living creatures in the water-filled pores between the individual grains of sand. The rich fauna of these minute cavities is distinguished by a whole series of significant structural and functional peculiarities which are clearly connected with the two essential extreme factors of the ground, namely the small size of the particles and the movement of the water. For one thing, in view of the small extent of the living space available inside the labyrinthine system of cavities, the size of its inhabitants is usually strikingly small. Large forms have a correspondingly small cross-section: wheel animals, flatworms, bottle animals, and isopods all have long, thin, thread-like bodies. Furthermore, the sand is liable to keep shifting, and many inhabitants of damp sand can cling to the particles of sand, with organs such as adhesive papillae, claws, or hooks.

As on the sea coast, the most important biological factors on the shores of lakes, ponds, and rivers are the maximum height the water reaches, the length of time any flooding lasts, and the structure of the ground. Here, too, sandy and muddy shores favour diggers, whereas stony and gravelly shores are completely devoid of tunnelling and tube-digging species. Insects, especially short-winged insects, and spiders, thanks to the waterproof nature of their bodies, their small weight, and their long legs or the enlargement of the surface of the

89

body by bristles, are able to cross the surface of the water and settle on newly formed banks and islands.

In this frontier region between water and land, conditions are always changing; every species of creature is continually forced to undertake small journeys in order to reach spots with the most favourable conditions. Nor must we underestimate the importance of the vegetation in these areas to creatures great and small. Thus in reed banks bird life is the most striking element in the fauna. In reeds and also in nearby meadows further inland movement poses special problems. Reed warblers hop skilfully with bodies erect

The otter emerges from the water and slips into its burrow. When it is looking for productive hunting-grounds this supple fish-eater does not shrink under certain circumstances from undertaking long trips on land.

between the reeds. The feet of bald coots, divers, diving ducks, and so forth either have broad fringes or else are completely webbed; it is the same with beavers, muskrats, water-shrews, and otters. Many birds of the river banks and water meadows are distinguished by stilt legs and long beaks. Herons, flamingos, cranes, and storks can wade a long way into water without wetting their feathers.

All in all, marshy river banks and lush, marshy meadows—unlike high-lying moorland and mossy tundras—are characterized by the wealth of the species they support; hardly one is missing. Vertebrates and snails, worms, insects, and spiders are all represented in amazing abundance. As there is enough moisture present in the upper layers of soil, the vegetation makes do with roots that do not spread very far, and on the whole the pressure of the cells (turgidity) suffices to keep the plant firmly in position—in contrast to the plants of the steppe, which often anchor themselves by mechanical props.

5 *Life in Light and Darkness*

THE PLANT—A CREATURE OF LIGHT

But for the sun's light our planet would be nothing but a ball of dead matter. All plant and animal life, except for the bacteria which live by chemosynthesis, is in the last analysis dependent on sunlight, which is the ultimate source of energy.

The ability to turn light into form and life, into buds, leaves, blossoms, and fruit, will always be one of the most wonderful characteristics of green plants. As a result of the lack of uniformity in the radiation of light, individual plants in their natural surroundings experience considerable differences in intensity. Most of them can live in widely varying degrees of light. A birch tree can still thrive with a ninth of full daylight, a beech with a sixtieth; wood sorrel can still develop in a hundredth part of the full light of day, liver mosses in a six-hundredth, ferns in a seventeen-hundredth, and deciduous mosses in a mere two-thousandth part.

Besides green plants, there are also plants that thrive on decay. They are not easy to recognize at first, for they hide in the shadiest spots where most humus accumulates; and they look pale and colourless. No genuine saprophyte is green, and none of them has any proper leaves, for they need very little light. This is the reason why we can find mushrooms growing in dark cellars and deep mine galleries.

Then there are other plants of the shade, most of them simple, unostentatious growths, living on the small fraction of sunlight which reaches the floor of a dense forest; every dull day, every cloud means that this small minimum of light is still further reduced. In many of these plants the leaves are flat and horizontal, and perhaps arranged in a mosaic, so as to make the best possible use of the light.

The differing adaptation to light of individual plants naturally has a considerable effect on the landscape and the nature of the various communities of plants. The division of the forest into trees, bushes, plants, and mosses, fungi and bacteria reflects the differing penetration of light. The trees enjoy full sunlight and therefore the greatest opportunities for assimilation. Only a fraction of the full light reaches the bushes, still less reaches the plants, and least of all reaches the layer of moss: in a light birch coppice it is a twentieth, under beeches and spruces only about a hundredth, and in the

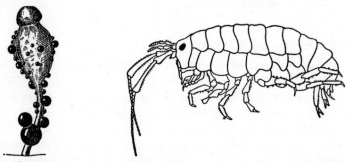

Left: Pilobolus, *the horse-manure fungus, greatly enlarged, just before its cap is hurled off. The function of the numerous drops and the mechanism of their excretion are unknown. Right:* Talitrus saltator, *the well-known sandhopper of the sea shore. Real size,* 15 *millimetres.*

tropical rain forest in some circumstances only a five-hundredth or even an eight-hundredth. Obviously plants that must have a good deal of light cannot live in such unfavourable conditions, and in fact in really thick forest other plants, including mosses, are limited to a few varieties that can stand deep shade. For example, in dense pine and fir forests, which hardly a ray of sunshine penetrates, there is only an evergreen layer of certain mosses.

In the mountains, light is distinguished by its great intensity, and in the polar regions it lasts for an exceptionally long time during summer. Here plants can carry on the process of assimilation not only in the daytime but also through the night. Thus within the space of a few months the vegetation of the cold polar regions can produce considerable quantities of matter. If these are nevertheless smaller than they would be in temperate latitudes, that is due not to the light but to the low temperature.

The growth movements in a plant stimulated by light are called phototropism. We speak of positive or negative reaction to light according to whether part of the plant grows towards or away from the source of light. Shoots are usually positively phototropic, roots on the other hand very often negatively phototropic.

A very small amount of light is sufficient to produce phototropic reactions. A reaction has been observed after a strong flash of light lasting only 1/2000 second, which indicates that a plant's sensitivity to light can be extreme. The same is true of the intensity of light: 1/500,000 lux is enough for bean seeds. Under certain circumstances even the phosphorescence of luminous bacteria can produce a phototropic effect.

DAYLIGHT, TWILIGHT, AND NOCTURNAL ANIMALS

All animals are dependent to some degree on light, no matter to what stage of organization or development they belong.

The interplay of light, moisture, and temperature in the formation of the pigments in many animals is noteworthy. The differences in colour of many insects before and after their winter repose show clearly that changes of colour can occur when the perfect insect first emerges, and consequently in the fully developed creature as well. When grasshoppers are in a dry environment and bright light the yellow, yellowish-red, and green pigments are largely destroyed and a certain amount of melanin is produced; as a result the creatures take on a brown colour. On the other hand, when the air is moister, the formation of lipochrome is encouraged and the creatures turn yellow. Dark surroundings, quite apart from the moisture in the air, cause an increase of melanin and lipochrome and make the green pigments disappear. In the reptiles, especially lizards, changes in colour are determined by the light in moderate temperatures, but by the temperature alone if it rises above or falls below this medium range.

A special form of orientation by light in certain animals involves their orienting themselves by the sun. Some sense of time is also involved, so that these animals can maintain a particular direction of travel and compensate for the changing position of the sun. This phenomenon is particularly well demonstrated by bees and by migrating birds.

Unlike plants, which can 'see' with their whole surface, animals possess only relatively small organs of sight intended for the reception of light rays. These organs range from the purple stigma of the unicellular flagellate, via the still fairly simple cup-shaped eye of a flatworm, to the compound eye of an insect and the complex eye of a vertebrate.

Small nocturnal animals often have well-rounded, if not completely spherical, lenses. Among the nocturnal mammals of Europe, dormice and ordinary mice possess relatively large lenses. The size

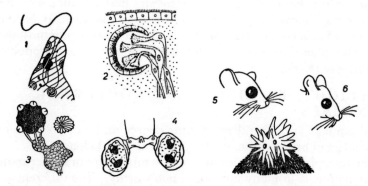

Light-sensing organs in various living creatures. 1. Spiracle (stigma) of a unicellular flagellate. 2. Sight organ of a flatworm with numerous sight-cells. 3. Eye body with optic ganglion, brain, and subsidiary eye of a crab. 4. Eye 'spectacles' of the amphibious mite Eylais (Tibet, South Africa). 5/6. Giant eyes of twilight animals: on the left a dormouse, on the right a yellow-necked mouse. 7. Head-section of the star-nosed mole: small eyes and a delicate rosette of fleshy feelers.

of the lens here determines the size of the eye, which in these rodents is noteworthy. The advantage of such spherical lenses rests in the fact that they light up the background.

Adaptations to dim light are not confined to the light-collecting apparatus of the eye; the retina, too, can show modifications in this direction. Thus the retinal rods, which are very sensitive to differences in the intensity of light, are exceptionally numerous in the retina of 'twilight' animals (gecko, hedgehog). The high sensitivity to light of these parts of the eye means that in stronger light they are over-stimulated and will not function. Hence the eyes of many 'twilight' animals possess a particularly effective protection against light in the pupil which is often cloven in form and can narrow itself right down or even close up altogether. Then there is the so-called tapetum, a layer of the retina in which numerous sparkling crystals are embedded. These reflect the rays of light that enter the eye, and thus the smallest quantities of light are put to use. This is why

94

cats' eyes shine in the dark. The same phenomenon in many insects and spiders is also caused by light-reflecting structures in the back of the eye.

Certain parallels are to be found in geckos, most of which are nocturnal. Not only is the cell structure of the retina different but the pupils are quite different from the sort usually found in lizards. In some nocturnal geckos the pupil, which is always vertical, forms a slit like a cat's; in other species the edges of the pupil have lobed bulges on both sides. When this pupil is contracted, four small apertures are produced, each of which throws its own picture on the retina.

In the European shrew and the African burrowing rat, the so-called naked mole, the eyes are tiny but the senses of smell and taste are highly developed. It is the same with the badger, which has strikingly small, not very sharp, eyes, but possesses big bristly feelers on the upper lip. The eyes of the genuine underground mammals are minute. A good example is the mole, whose tiny eyes are covered by the hairs of its fur and are decidedly rudimentary. Bigger eyes would certainly be a disadvantage in burrowing; but it is clear that its existing eyes are not entirely useless, for if danger threatens a mole when it is above ground they emerge from the fur like black beads and the animal hurries off towards the nearest hiding place, which it could not find without the help of its eyesight. However, the mole's indubitably weak eyes are more than adequately balanced by its exceptionally keen senses of smell and touch.

A curious relation of the European mole is the North American star-nosed mole, a rough-haired fellow with huge shovel-shaped hands and incredibly small eyes. On the front of its pointed head, round the tip of the snout, lies a bright pink, very mobile and partly retractable fleshy appendix. There can be no doubt that this sensitive rosette is an organ of touch, which allows the star-mole, an inhabitant of damp soil near water, to find its way in the dark.

Those tiny subterranean creatures the mites are very interesting in this connection. Their eyes are minute and the sense of touch is extremely strongly developed. In the species with a strong armour of chitin the hairs on the body and legs are organs of touch. Their greatly varying number and mode of attachment, and the functionally determined variety of their forms—branching, feathered, toothed, flattened, cylindrical, or club-shaped—provide the best possible means of making the mites aware of what is going on around them. Mites that live in the layers of rotting vegetation on top of

95

the ground and in the bigger cavities and clefts in the soil react in a special way to stimuli from outside. Some species can draw in their legs and close up the front and back of their bodies like a lid, so that they look like a grain of seed. Other mites possess chitin flaps on each side like wings, under which they can tuck their legs when disturbed. This simulation of death enables many mites to escape their enemies.

Besides hairs on the body which function as organs of touch, many mites possess what are known as 'pseudo-stigmatic organs', pairs of excrescences situated on the rear edge of the back and appearing in all kinds of forms, from simple hairs to thick, whip-like organelles shaped like leaves, fans, balls, cylinders, or rods. They may have several branches, they may be thickly covered with bristles or smooth, but in every case they react to temperature and moisture, and possibly also to sound waves. These striking sense organs are so constant and so characteristic of mites that they play quite an important rôle in the classification of the various genera and species.

Some creatures that dig or burrow have special protections for the openings of their ears and eyes, especially the latter. The lower eyelid of most lizards is movable, opaque, and covered with scales, but in many sand skinks it consists of a transparent plate. With this 'window' these burrowing lizards can protect their eyes against sand and dust, yet still be in a position to see at least something of their surroundings. In the fringe-toed lizards, which are natives of North America, the eyes are protected by lids consisting of projecting scales when the creature is digging in the sand. Similarly, the horned 'toads' (lizards) of the steppes and deserts of central Asia, which are excellent diggers, protect themselves successfully against the danger of sand penetrating their eyes by means of a kind of gutter of over-hanging scales above their eyes; these scales act as eyebrows. In addition, the edge of the eyelid is fitted with long scaly spines; they protect the eyes from any sand that trickles down, while the fringe-like 'eyelashes' wipe away the dust which the desert wind blows over the ground. In the subterranean blind snakes, and their relatives the burrowing snakes, the tiny eyes are hidden away under big scales, through which they can just be seen shimmering like dull shadows.

AN ISOLATED EXISTENCE IN ETERNAL DARKNESS

Cave biotopes represent more or less isolated habitats, for they are almost completely exempt from the daily and seasonal fluctuations of

This aerial photograph gives a good idea of the virgin forest's luxuriant splendour. A small river makes its way through the tropical forest. (Photo: R. Gardi/Bavaria.)

The roots of huge trees grow over the temple of Taprohm in the ruined city of Angkor in Cambodia. (Photo: K. T. Fritsche/Bavaria.)

the outside world; temperatures are constant and mostly low, the moisture content of the air is uniformly high, sources of food are scarce and poor, and light is completely absent. Animal life in this subterranean world includes forms which have not changed since the geological Middle Ages.

Green plants are bound to be absent, for they must have light for photosynthesis; but we find fungi, which flourish in caves on the droppings of animals and in mines on rotting wood. The ground and sides of the approaches to caves are quite often covered with layers of shimmering, bluish-green algae and variegated carpets of moss; the trickles of water down the walls of caves show 'ink strokes'—blackish coats of algae and lichens; and growths as hard as stone are created by the activity of lime-secreting algae at spots where water drips down. Even in the very dark parts of caves and galleries we sometimes find green mosses and ferns, and various blue and green algae. This shows clearly that the building-up of organic matter by photosynthesis can go on even in caves, if only to a very slight degree.

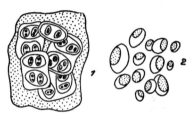

Cave algae. 1. *Gelatinous deposit of* Gloeocapsa (*blue alga*). 2. Protococ-cus (*green alga*).

The low level of development or complete absence of eyes is noticeable in all cave-dwelling creatures. This is demonstrated by the flatworms and scuds, which live underground in muddy soil, and also by isopods, which are not completely blind. As a matter of fact, isopods enable us to see very clearly the transition from creatures that live in the light to those of the dark; they differ according to whether we take examples from the entrance to a cave or from further inside. The eyes of the varieties that can see are small and pigmented; while in the species from deep inside caves the eyes have disappeared completely, without leaving even a trace behind. In so far as amphibians occur in caves—salamanders do, for example—their eyes, too, show varying degrees of development, down to the point of complete blindness. If the eyes of the young amphibians are noticeably better developed than those of the adult animals, that is because the process of modification begins in the post-embryonic period.

The influence of environmental conditions on mode of life, form, physical shape, and functioning of the organs is demonstrated most

G

vividly, so far as underground insects are concerned, by the beetles which live in the caves of European mountains, especially the Alps and the Karst region of Yugoslavia. They are mostly blind or equipped with only rudimentary eyes; and the lack of light has led to an extensive loss of pigment in their chitinous armour, a phenomenon which also occurs in underground scuds, isopods, mites, flat-worms, and newts. The cave beetles' feelers have become longer, and instead of eyes they have feeler-bristles, some of them on the neck casing and elytra (front wings).

Most of the organic life in the soil goes on in the topmost layers. The varying need for light regulates the distribution of the organisms and allows classification into zones. Many surface creatures—snails,

Cave and grotto dwellers. 1. Desmoscolex, *a threadworm which because of its unusual appearance was earlier taken for an arthropod larva.* 2. Aphaenopsis, *an underground beetle. This small, clumsy ground beetle is not a predator like its relations on the surface, but a real detritus-eater; its jaws are correspondingly tender.*

beetles, spiders, mites, simple insects and so forth—are decidedly afraid of light; in the daytime they stay in the rotting vegetation, under the bark of decaying tree trunks, under stones, and so on, and only become active in search of food at night. The rest of the life in the soil is situated to all intents and purposes inside the zone traversed by roots—the so-called rhizosphere. Between twelve and twenty inches down one still finds fungoid tissues, bacteria, and blue algae. Farther down the lower forms of life are on the whole hardly found; this is true not only of areas where there is no deep layer of humus; it is just the same in regions where the humus is many feet deep, such as the chernozem or black earth belts of the Ukraine, Hungary, Rumania, and North America.

Another characteristic of creatures that live in the ground is a certain poverty of pigmentation. In general, strong colours like black and dark brown are confined to inhabitants of the layers of moss and rotting vegetation on the surface. Mites, beetles, and millipedes are usually light brown, while the typical colour of primitive insects and many isopods is grey, which becomes pure white in species living deeper down. Few creatures of the soil are distinguished by vivid colours. In certain circumstances mites can vary considerably in their colouration according to soil and climate. We are familiar with gleaming scarlet species that live on the surface and with bright red to orange ones from deeper strata. Some springtails are lemon-yellow, others green to bluish-green. The lower edaphic organisms, such as infusoria, threadworms, and wheel animals, are absolutely colourless; only a few are distinguished by a brighter colouring.

In regular inhabitants of the ground, as in cave-dwelling animals, changes in the eyes are to be observed. As we have already indicated, the eyes of moles, marsupial moles, and mole-rats are exceptionally small. Other inhabitants of the soil—simple insects, moss mites, ground beetles, millipedes, threadworms, and earthworms—lack eyes completely. Instead they often have highly sensitive organs of touch.

6 *Food and Nourishment*

Any organism requires specific food substances for its metabolism. The choice of food is closely bound up with biochemical changes and rests only to a slight extent on experience. Food forms an important environmental factor in the lives of all animals.

Some kinds of animals can manage for a very long time without food. At the Zoological Institute in Rostock ticks have been kept alive without food for eighteen years. Like other inhabitants of deserts and dry regions, lizards can endure long periods of hunger when they can find no food. Obviously, during the course of such fasts, which often last for months, they lose considerably in weight and grow much thinner. This is particularly noticeable in the appearance of the tail; within a month this normally substantial appendage can lose a fifth of its bulk.

The ability to withstand hunger is often dependent on climatic influences. Cold or extreme drought often compels animals either to move on—one has only to think of the wanderings of reindeer or antelope—or to reduce the vital functions severely by hibernating or going rigid. The alpine marmot and the dormouse can live for up to six months without food when they are hibernating. Another rodent, the ground squirrel, takes no food for about 160 days; during this period of hibernation its rate of breathing drops from thirty times a minute to once a minute.

As soon as their surroundings cease to provide sufficient water, certain animals—the edible snail, for example—fall into a summer sleep without any stock of food at all; the members of a South African species of solitary bee can exist for two to three years in a state of rigidity with a reduced rate of metabolism. It is known that the African lungfish can live for as long as four years sealed up eighteen inches deep in hard, dry mud, losing a good third of its weight in the process. Unicellular organisms can seal themselves up in cysts in dried-up cracks in the ground; wheel animals, and bear animalcules living in cushions of moss, can go rigid in dry conditions and stay alive in a state of suspended animation for up to ten years.

How do animals actually find the particular kind of food that suits them and corresponds to their needs? First of all, it is essential that the sense organs should react effectively to smell, taste, movement, and other stimuli. Food is accepted or rejected according to its characteristics. For example, with the help of its 'antennae' the dung beetle becomes aware of its food at distances of up to five yards when the wind is favourable; it is the same with the trumpet snail, which feeds on dead and decaying animal matter. On the other hand, flesh-eating animals (especially insect eaters) can be described as the 'visual type'; they react primarily to movement. To many creatures, mere warmth can be a sign of food; this is true, for example, of mosquitoes and lice, which suck the blood from birds or mammals.

In general, these indications of food are not acted upon when the animal is replete; there must be a certain degree of hunger before an animal seeks or devours food.

If the hunger is great and the normal food is lacking, the animal will often try to eat something that it normally refuses, even things that are not food at all. A good example of this is the shrew, which has a very high rate of metabolism and in consequence will stuff itself with anything eatable, whether animal or plant, living or dead, fresh or decayed—including its own young and members of its own species when other food is short. Genuinely omnivorous creatures, such as the cockroach, will eat anything—bread, sugar, meat, cheese, paper, shoe polish, and even their own sloughed-off skin. If no food at all is obtainable and the creature begins to starve, it uses up fat and other substances present in the body to keep itself alive.

Hamster's head with full cheek pouches.

Many animals keep reserve supplies. African sleeping mice, which often take over the abandoned communal nests of certain species of spiders, accumulate extensive stocks of food: unripe fruit, nuts, dead insects, and even small birds. An example nearer home is the hamster, which builds several larders next to the well-upholstered living space in its underground burrow. Into these larders it carries, as supplies for the winter, large quantities of wheat, beans, and other seeds, all with the help of the big pouches in its cheeks.

THE BILL OF FARE

Some animals will, if need be, devour anything indiscriminately, some stick to one kind of food, and some periodically change their diet, either in accordance with the rhythm of their own life or with that of the seasons. Most animals have a favourite food, which they eat whenever it is freely and naturally available. The longer the possible bill of fare, the greater chance the animal has of eating its fill and thus of surviving in the struggle to live.

The most varied menu is that of the omnivorous animals, the ones which feed on both animal and vegetable matter. The badger eats small mammals, lizards, worms, and insects as well as green plants, fruit, fungi, and roots. Another animal that is genuinely omnivorous is the American pouched rat, which eats insects and other small creatures as well as carrion, greenstuff, and fruit; it also often displays cannibalistic inclinations. The European wild boar eats acorns, nuts, turnips, and potatoes; it turns up the soil for fern roots and crops the grass; and it also devours small mammals up to and including young deer, carrion of every sort, snakes, snails, worms, chrysalises, and grubs. Not many insects are omnivorous, though termites can digest a good many different things and cockroaches, as we have noted, will eat almost anything.

Among land animals, herbivorous or plant-eating species are by far the most numerous. Lower plants, such as fungi, lichens, and algae, are eaten primarily by snails and insects. The higher plants are the basic food of the two predominant groups of land creatures, the insects and the mammals (hoofed animals, rodents, apes), which are in some respects particularly well adapted to the extraction and destruction of complicated plant tissues. Insects either chew up the tissues or break them off and suck or eat out the inside; we know that simple insects and the larvae of beetles and flies do the latter. There are many which eat wood. Sappy wood is devoured by the larvae of the *Buprestis* or burn-cow beetle, weevils and the powder-pest beetle; the larvae of many beetles gnaw away at the dividing line between bark and wood; and rotting wood harbours the larvae of the *Buprestis* beetle and of weevils. They are all capable of breaking down cellulose, the main constituent of wood, which most groups of animals cannot digest. They manage this with the help of ferments produced in their own bodies, while in other wood-eaters, such as termites which are such an important factor in the tropics, the task is accomplished by symbiotic unicellular organisms including bacteria.

On the whole, the best known of the herbivorous land animals are naturally the hoofed mammals, many of which man has domesticated. Others, such as wild cattle, antelope, zebras, and giraffes, still live on the grasslands of Africa, Asia, and North America. These wild herbivorous animals wander about in big herds in search of food and in a short time can completely destroy the vegetation of a given area. Herds of bison a million strong once roamed the wide prairies of North America. Travellers in Africa have recalled the huge herds of springboks which broke into Cape Colony from the Kalahari in the middle of the last century.

No less dependent on plants for their food are the rodents, a very varied group of animals. Many species cause as much damage to plants as insects do.

The carnivores which make particular animals their prey devour the whole tissue and the organs. For instance, certain mammals specialize in ants and termites. Among these are the Australian marsupial ant-eater, the aardvark and aardwolf of the African savannah, the scaly ant-eater of the damp virgin forests of southern Asia, and the ant-bear or great ant-eater. The tamandua, which is somewhat smaller than the great ant-eater, can tuck away every day the contents of a termite nest eighteen inches square. It tears open the nest with powerful heaves of its claws and sticks its long tube-shaped jaw into the opening; then out shoots its tongue like a thin eighteen-inch snake and picks up the insects and their larvae, which are trapped on its sticky upper surface.

Most of the reptiles are carnivorous. Many tortoises devour frogs, snails, insects, and worms, and lizards do the same. Snakes eat mammals, birds, fish, amphibians, worms, and snails. Carnivorous habits take various forms in insects. The killing of the prey may precede the eating or it may coincide with it; or again, the prey may just be paralysed, so that it can be kept fresh for quite a long time and consumed by degrees. Some species of wasp do this. With predatory insects there is an interesting relation between the nature of the prey and the way in which it is caught, which may be by jumping (jumping grasshopper), by running, by flying leap, or by ambush. Tropical bugs are adapted to their particular mode of feeding by the modification of their front legs into implements for snatching, grasping and pinching. Other lurking predators are the ant-lion and the tiger-beetle, which set up funnel-shaped traps in the sand and catch small insects, especially ants.

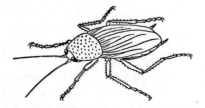

Male of the common European cockroach
(Blatta orientalis).

The ant-lion, of worldwide distribution, is decidedly a 'stenotope'—that is, tied to a small area—in that it arranges its traps where there is uniformly fine, dry, and therefore easily movable, sand to be found, principally under the overhanging edges of caves and ridges facing south in the northern hemisphere and north in the southern. In the preparation of the sand trap the body penetrates into the sand, while the forward-pointing legs push the larva backwards over the ground and the back end pushes against the ground. Then the ant-lion throws the sand up over itself with its front end and thus gradually builds a regular funnel, whose size is quite independent of the size of the body and increases in proportion to the length of time the creature has gone hungry.

Certain communities of ants—especially in tropical countries—which only build nests in the most exceptional circumstances, lead a wild, uncertain, nomadic life. Among them are the *Anomma* ants

Larva of the Myrmeleon; *the ant-lion,
a native of Central and Southern Europe.*

of East Africa, which undertake regular plundering raids. Their hordes inspire panic in all kinds of creatures—insects, worms, amphibians, and mice. Anything that they get their sharp jaws into is left behind as a skeleton.

The amounts of food which land animals eat are amazing. A mole weighing scarcely $2\frac{3}{4}$ ounces can devour up to $4\frac{1}{4}$ ounces of earthworms, which is $\frac{1}{4}$ ounce dry weight; hedgehogs weighing 32$\frac{1}{4}$ ounces are known to eat 2$\frac{1}{2}$ ounces dry weight of meal-worms every day. In the forests of Siberia, the polecat, weasel, and ermine live mainly on voles. Ringing has shown that, as a result, 40 per cent of the voles, whose normal life span is three to five years, live for only about ten days, 28 per cent for 20 days, 20 per cent for a month, 9 per cent for 40 days, and only 3 per cent for 50 days. In the stomach of a 5-foot-long North American bull-adder 35 small mice were

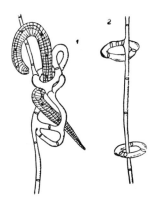

Arthrobotrys, *a fungus that catches thread-worms*. 1. *A* Bunonema *worm has been caught in the fungus's net. The fungus sends hyphae into the nematode's body, and these hyphae gradually suck it dry.* 2. *Predatory fungus's nooses for catching its prey.*

found; another contained a clutch of four eggs laid by a species of sparrow that nests on the ground, four just-hatched birds, four half-grown ones, and four almost fully fledged ones.

A number of plants feed on flesh. So far as the lower plants are concerned, the main examples of this are predatory thread fungi, which lie in wait for threadworms and then, with organs specially created for this purpose, kill them and suck them dry. Humus with plenty of decayed vegetable matter in it is usually very thickly populated by these fungi, so that some threadworms, which are also present in large quantities—there are some four or five million to the square yard in meadowland—are bound to keep coming into contact with them. The trapping devices consist either of globular heads, which grow out of the mycelium on a runner, or of nooses formed in the thread of fungus and corresponding roughly in diameter to the thickness of a worm. At the point of contact the fungus emits a poisonous secretion which destroys the skin of its prey. A thread of fungus immediately enters the wound, swells up into a globe, and sends further threads through the worm's whole body, which is then completely sucked out.

In higher plants capable of catching and digesting small animals, leaves or parts of leaves are modified in various different ways and serve in most cases both as organs for catching and for digesting. In the sundew and the butterwort the principle of the fly-paper is applied, in tropical pitcher plants that of the pitfall. In the species which grow at ground level and are hidden in the humus of the virgin forest, a digestive juice is secreted inside the pitcher and this juice breaks down the protein of the creature captured. A pepsin is involved which, like the pepsin in an animal's stomach, works only in an acid solution. Consequently acids too (formic acid and citric acid among others) are secreted by the plant; these also keep bacteria at a distance and thus prevent the captive prey from decaying.

Numerous creatures, both above and below ground, live on the waste products of animals, on dung, urine, and excrement of every kind, which contains half-digested and undigested foodstuffs, slime, bile, and a bacterial flora. Sometimes dung is only an emergency food, as in the case of the arctic fox, which will eat the droppings of polar bears, especially in the confined spaces of an island. However, many creatures are regular specialists in animal waste products; good examples are the larvae of many flies and above all the well-known dung beetles.

The individual species of the latter reflect a remarkably high stage of development in the case of their young. Many of them lay their eggs direct into cowpats; others construct a whole system of tunnels and channels in which the eggs are housed, passages which lead from the heap of dung straight down into the ground and end in side passages and dung-filled hatching spaces, each occupied by one egg. In this way the larvae are not only provided with food but also housed in well-protected spaces that will not dry out.

The evolution of the method of looking after the young in the various species of dung beetle is interesting. At first the eggs were laid on the surface of the dung, then simple or branching tunnels and special incubating chambers with walls of dung were built. To start with, the stock of dung was left in a crude state, but later the dung was thoroughly kneaded and divided up into little pills. This process of development reaches its climax in the 'pill-rollers', especially the famous *Scarabaeus* species. In ancient Egypt the scarab was the sun god's sacred creature. The Egyptians imagined that a celestial dung beetle rolled the sun in front of it, just as the earthly one rolls a ball of dung. The 'pill-rollers' mould the dung into balls, which they roll away and bury underground, where they use them as pear-shaped 'hatching pellets.' The egg is enclosed in the small end of the pear in a special airy chamber. When the larva hatches it begins to eat the dung, which is damp inside its earth-encrusted rind and is prevented from drying out through being buried in the ground (in a perpendicular tunnel some four inches deep). By the time the full-grown beetle is ready to emerge the pellet is hard and dry, and the scarab has to wait to creep out until the autumn rain has softened the ground and moistened the pellet.

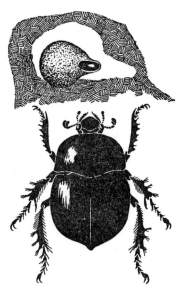

Some ants live on the secretions of the caterpillars of the Large Blue butterfly, of leaf lice and shield lice, and of cicadas. Indeed, for many ants—the sand ant, for example—the sugary secretions of the Large Blue caterpillars, which are kept in the nest, are supposed to form the chief form of nourishment. A similar relationship exists between termites and certain bugs. Threadworms and mites live in dung heaps, and the larvae of many house flies live in the dung of ruminants and in chicken and horse manure. The grubs of some rove beetles live in cow dung.

Scarabaeus, *the 'sacred pill-roller'.* Above: *open pear-shaped 'hatching pellet', with the egg at the front end.*

Certain infusoria live on the dung and urine of amphibians, and occasionally wheel animals are found in the gut of earthworms and snails.

Year after year, as part of an everlasting cycle, the plant world produces a huge quantity of organic material. Only a very small fraction of this is fixed in the bodies of animals; most of it falls a victim to decay—that is, it is broken down again by micro-organisms into the basic substances from which it was built up and is returned directly to the cycle. Everywhere where the remains of animals and plants decay and are further broken down by soil organisms, humus comes into being. It lends the upper strata of the ground a dark, blackish-brown colour. The greatest abundance of humus is found in marshy ground.

An important part in the formation of humus is played by earthworms, which are found everywhere except in the Antarctic and on Madagascar and are divided by zoologists into several genera, from the common or garden earthworm to the Australian 'earthworm snake', *Megascolides*, which is sometimes over three yards long! Some worms live in putrefying matter and others again prefer only partially decayed wood and vegetation, but most of them work on the organic refuse in the ground, literally eating their way through the soil and thus thoroughly mixing organic and mineral elements. Some species, especially the big, strong ones, are in the

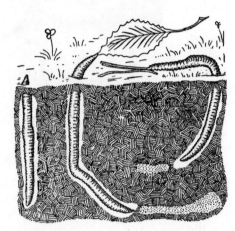

Earthworms can pull leaves and pine needles into the ground.

habit of pulling only partially decayed vegetation, and sometimes even living parts of plants, into their tunnels at night and of moistening them with a slimy secretion which seems to encourage decay.

When the process of decay through the action of bacteria has reached the right stage, the substances are consumed, together with the micro-organisms, bacteria, algae, and protozoa living on them. But only a small proportion is digested; the rest are still alive when they leave the gut. The passage of the material through the worm, in which it is not only mechanically pulverized but also chemically transformed, leads to the formation of humus.

In steppe areas the rôle of the earthworms is taken over, as we have already indicated, by rodents—pouched rats, barking squirrels, ground squirrels, and similar creatures. In many places in New Zealand communities of tuataras and various species of stormy petrel are responsible for the creation of humus. The birds nest in underground holes, which they share harmoniously with the lizards.

Often there are three to four such nesting places in one square yard, and the ground is then traversed by a system of subterranean passages. Leaves and twigs are blown into these passages by the prevailing wind and thoroughly mixed with the soil by the birds' continual burrowing. Thus at a depth of about eighteen inches foliage, twigs, feathers, egg-shells, and the excrement of the lizards and birds are all thoroughly mixed together. When microbial transformation has taken place, this mixture forms loose, exceptionally fertile humus.

Here we must mention guano, the excrement of sea birds, which is piled up sometimes to a height of 250 feet on the arid coasts of Peru and Chile, and has been highly prized as manure since the time of the Incas because of its nitrogen and phosphorus content. These immense heaps of guano are explained by the density of the bird population, which consists mainly of cormorants and gannets. One single colony of gannets can contain over 120,000 birds, and in the course of a year these birds produce 400 tons of guano. Sea birds of the Peruvian and Chilean coasts, which would find few opportunities for nesting on the bare cliffs, dig their nests in the huge piles of manure.

Humus is very rich in micro-organisms. The quantity varies considerably from one layer of the soil to another and also according to the nature of the humus; there are fewer of these organisms in sour, badly aerated, and very dry soil than in well-aerated, moist soil. Only 3/100 ounce of fertile soil can contain well over a thousand million micro-organisms, which together with innumerable larger organisms populate the upper layers of the ground. Thus in a thimbleful of good arable soil as many micro-organisms are active as there are people on the whole earth.

The total volume of the micro-organisms present in 3/100 ounce of earth has been estimated at only 12/1000 cubic inch, but the total surface area of this amount of soil is about 16 square inches! That will serve as a measure of the activity of these micro-organisms. If we make allowance for the fact that the number of organisms declines at the deeper levels, 2½ acres of good farm land contain about 1000 pounds of micro-organisms, while the weight of big livestock on the same area amounts on an average to 250 pounds. The total surface area of the micro-organisms living in 2½ acres of farm land amounts to more than 2500 acres!

It has long been realized that all these soil organisms are by no means insignificant. They do not lead exclusively predatory or parasitic lives; on the contrary, their activity is an extremely helpful, indeed indispensable, link in the general scheme of things, and is needed for the formation of fertile soil.

GULPING—CHEWING—SCRAPING—SUCKING

No creatures, apart from the parasites, receive their food automatically; they have to seek it out. In carnivorous animals, the whole apparatus of movement is adapted to hunting. The wolf, which is a swift and tireless runner, courses its prey. The cheetah,

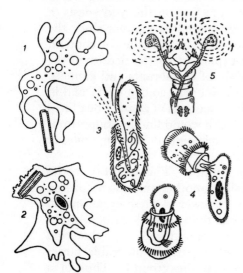

Methods of Feeding in Lower Organisms

1/2. *Surrounding and swallowing of food in amoebas.*

3. *Infusoria devour particles: cilia sweep them in; food passes through oral groove or gullet; waste is expelled through cell anus.*

4. *A* Didinium *infusorium swallows a slipper animalcule. The prey is seized and crippled by the cilia of the gullet. Inside the cell it is enclosed in a food vacuole.*

5. *A bdelloid wheel animal sweeps in food particles with the help of the mouth mechanism.*

on the other hand, stalks its victim and only breaks into its furious gallops for the last hundred yards in the final attack. It is probably the fastest of the quadrupeds, for it can easily overtake antelopes and gazelles, which reach over sixty miles an hour when they are going at full speed. The physical build of the jackal makes it a true carrion eater; thanks to its medium-length legs and slender, supple body, the fox is an excellent creeper, while the anatomical structure of the marten and the exceptional sharpness of its senses make it creeper, jumper, and climber all in one. With its long, cylindrical body and stumpy legs the weasel is quick and skilful at worming its way into the burrows of mice and hamsters.

Fundamentally, the situation is much the same with the tiny creatures that live in the ground. Let us take the example of the wheel animals. Many of them eat only moulds, bacteria, and algae, but their ranks also include predators, carrion eaters, and parasites. So far as choice of food is concerned, some are omnivorous, others specialize in one particular kind. Even cannibalism is quite common. Wheel animals can be divided into those which digest their food externally and those which digest it internally. As for the way in which they get their food, three different types can be distinguished: the 'catchers' wait for their prey to pass by, the 'whirlers'—above all the leech-like varieties—take the food that comes into the circular eddies of their cilia, and the 'snatchers' actively seek out their prey. The chewing apparatus of the 'whirlers' resembles a flax-brake that claps together, while the 'snatchers' have a pincer device that executes chiselling or snapping movements. Species which concentrate on algae—blue algae, for example—push the filament down the oesophagus into the stomach like a sword-swallower and then nip it off at the top. Parasitic wheel animals are not very common, but they have been found on isopods, worms, and the larvae of insects, and also in the outer cells of mosses and in algae. One species is known to eat carrion; it is often found in large quantities among the corpses of its fellows, whose empty armour it devours.

The actual mechanics of eating vary enormously; the examples that follow have been chosen because of their relevance to the theme of this book.

First, there are the gulpers, which are in the habit of taking in relatively large lumps of food without breaking it up. Protozoa swallow their food (of animal or vegetable origin) either by simply enveloping it as amoebas do—the primitive form of all food absorption—or by swallowing it with the aid of mouth-like organelles.

Multi-cellular creatures have developed all kinds of devices with which to overcome their prey. Take the microscopically small wheel animals, for example: we find as many variations in the form of their chitinous jaws as there are species of these tiny creatures. On closer study, each variation turns out to be a biological prototype of a tool for seizing, holding, cutting, pricking, or grinding. We meet forms which might serve as patterns for hammer and anvil, awl, knife, shears, file, pincers, and dozens of other such tools. Flatworms and some predatory edaphic worms have a very complicated muscular oesophagus equipped with hooks, bristles, and teeth.

The 'gulpers' among the land vertebrates have a mouth that claps together and trap-like teeth. In snakes and other reptiles the mouth is enabled to open very wide by an adjustable lower jaw and extensible muscles and ligaments.

The tongues of many vertebrates are used for catching prey; for example, the gecko's tongue is equipped with adhesive and harpoon, while the cave salamander and the chameleon dart their tongues out —the latter to a distance of nearly ten inches. The ant-eaters—for instance, the well-known ant-bear—have special 'limed' tongues.

There is one special kind of eating technique which requires slippery food, such as earthworms and snails. The slow-worm lives on these. Its teeth are pointed and bent backwards, so that they do not grind anything up but instead penetrate the slimy covering of a snail or worm and hold the creature fast until it can be sucked

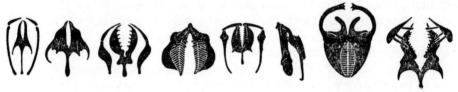

Chewing mechanisms of various wheel animals (Rotifera), *from the simplest to the most perfectly constructed type.*

down into the oesophagus. On the other hand, grass snakes, which are relatives of the slow-worm, have a characteristic 'nutcracker bite' that grinds their prey to pieces.

In all 'gulping' animals the act of gulping necessitates a complicated swallowing apparatus as well as modifications of the jaw and teeth and the presence of specific muscles, nerves, and sense organs. This again demands a special secretion of fluids and slimes with which to moisten food that is not naturally slippery and to swallow or suck it down whole.

When it comes to proper chewing, animals' teeth are wonderfully adapted to dealing with their food. Hardly any other part of an animal's body is so well adapted to prevailing conditions or gives us such a clear picture, even after death, of a creature's mode of life. We need to find only one or two teeth of a long-extinct animal in order to be able to say with certainty what kind of food it lived on.

Millions of years ago, in Jurassic and Cretaceous times, lived the dinosaurs, some of them dangerous predators, others harmless vegetarians. The *Tyrannosaurus*, for example, with its fantastic dimensions—it was almost certainly the most powerful and terrible

A typical steppe-land covered with thorn bushes (South West Africa.) (Photo: Dr Schulze, Bavaria.)

Tangle of stilt roots in a mangrove swamp. (Photo: P. Popper.)

carnivore that has ever inhabited our planet—had a murderous pair of jaws, with sabre teeth almost eight inches long. In contrast there was the *Brontosaurus*, a huge thirty-ton vegetarian ten times as heavy as a bull elephant, with a snake-like neck and a tiny head containing only a few poor, spoon-shaped teeth and a miserable little brain.

How mammals bite. 1. *Molars of a herbivorous animal (ox) and* 2. *of a carnivorous animal (cat)*. 3. *Lower jaw of the* Dinotherium, *an early relative of the elephant.* 4. *Elephant's molar, with the enamel bitten away to an increasing extent towards the back. Development of mammal's bite from the insect-eater (a) and herbivorous rodent (b) via the hoofed herbivore (c) and the beast of prey (d) ultimately to the 'mixed bite' of the primates (not shown.)*

In the *Iguanodon*, Cretaceous dinosaur, the tip of the snout was encircled by a horny beak as sharp as a knife. The jaws contained 90 teeth that were sharper still, and behind them rows of spare teeth. The big toes of the forefeet were pointed like powerful daggers, and with these the creature ploughed up the earth and pulled out nourishing roots, for this pot-belly was a harmless vegetarian!

What an immensely long chain of evolution leads from the first shrew-like insect-eaters—primitive hedgehogs and marsupials—via the first predators and awkwardly built herbivores up to today! In

H

the animals that chew their food in their mouths, there are many transitional stages between the weak molars of the small cats and the clearly differentiated molars of the herbivores.

Many creatures chew their food in their stomachs instead of in their mouths. Here, too, we find every possible stage of development, from the simple masticating stomach of the earthworm and the snail with their chewing plates to the extremely complicated arrangements to be found in many arthropods (earwigs, crickets, ground beetles, and others). The whole inside wall of these mechanisms for masticating bears a fine chitinous skin, on which are formations of chitin which vary in shape and arrangement from creature to creature: triangular plates with thorny projections and buckles, or coral-shaped teeth—often real works of art, which act as internal teeth, continuing the work of the jaws and effecting a thorough mixture with the gastric juices.

In the scaly animals which eat ants and termites complicated arrangements of stomach muscles move strong, horny plates like millstones. These stomachs can be amazingly powerful: that of the mangrove crab, for example, can grind the hardest mollusc shells to a fine powder.

The scrapers, too, have developed all kinds of tools and mechanisms for crushing up their food. Some use the rasping action of a file. One has only to think of a snail's tongue, which is a plate equipped with hook-shaped teeth. It rests on a muscular cartilage and can be moved by numerous muscles. The tiny teeth, which are arranged in rows, lengthways and obliquely, and which can vary in number from relatively few to many thousands (up to 125,000), often show, in their varying shapes, a clear relation to the way in which some particular food is obtained or to the food itself.

The teeth of rodents and hyraxes work on the principle of the knife and chisel; they are implements for cutting. Turtles have a beak rather like a bird's, with long cutting edges to the jaws.

The jaws of some creatures are constructed to cut like shears: for example, the multi-pointed molars of the insect-eaters, which can cut through hard chitin; the slanting molars with serrated edges of South American opossums and Australian rock-climbing marsupials, which feed mainly on succulents and roots; and above all the bone-shears of the carnivorous predatory mammals, in which a pair of teeth above and below form proper shears. For example, there is the Australian marsupial wolf; with 46 teeth in its jaws, which can be opened to 180 degrees, it possesses the most terrifying bite of all the

114

land mammals. The bite of a baboon is as effective as that of a leopard, and the jaws of a hyena form a powerful pair of shears with which the strongest marrow bones can be easily crushed, to be swallowed in splinters the length of a man's finger.

Some land creatures use limbs as shears for cutting up their food; this is the case with scorpions and harvestmen. The shepherd spiders of the tropics can tear a snail out of its shell in separate pieces with their powerful pincers. If the creature cannot reach its prey because the snail has gone in too far, then it shatters and crushes the shell with its jaws. The duck-billed platypus, too, squashes its prey with the plates of its horny beak, with which it roots about in muddy ground for worms, snails, and the larvae of insects.

A large number of creatures digest their food externally, by breaking up and dissolving their food with ferments. Certain gall fly larvae release the secretion of their saliva glands over wood and thus dissolve it. Quite often animals use auxiliary tools to inject the ferment and soften up the food. Spiders hold their food, moistened with saliva, in their mouths and knead it with the juices which will dissolve it. Scorpions sink their upper and lower lips in caterpillars, inject gastric juices, and suck their prey dry in less than a quarter of a minute. The carrion beetle *Phosphuga* mostly attacks slugs. It splashes its prey with a corrosive juice, ejected from the gut, which helps to digest it. The slug has no protection against this attack except its envelope of slime. Therefore the process of digestion is preceded by a softening of strips of the slug's skin; when the slug's body is sufficiently dissolved the beetles and their larvae drink up the loathsome liquid.

The big ground beetle, too, releases its gastric juice over the creatures rendered defenceless by its poisonous bite. When dissolution is complete, it drinks up the resulting liquid. Even mice caught in traps have been seen to perish in this way. The head was bitten, and an amazingly wide area round the bite was then transformed into a pappy mass.

Ground beetles and *Phosphuga* beetles can eat so much that they swell up and lie around for hours in the most curious attitudes while they digest their food. They stick the backs of their bodies up at an angle and their heads down to the ground, with the forelegs bent underneath and the hind-legs stiffly spread out. They remain in this attitude until they are hungry again.

We meet the principle of 'external digestion' again in the preparation of 'ant bread' by corn ants. The contents of the seeds brought into the nest are chewed up in hours of communal work; from the ants' mouths flow large quantities of saliva, which converts the starch into sugar. One seed has to be chewed by about a hundred workers for two full days. The 'ant bread' prepared in this way is consumed either fresh or after being kept for some time. When it is actually eaten it becomes softer and softer, and the converted sugar soon dissolves and disappears in the ant's crop.

Of course, besides the possible ways of eating already described there are all kinds of combinations. Many vertebrates are both

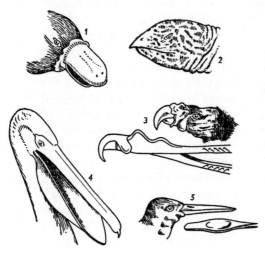

The biotechnology of the beak. (1) 'Duck's beak' of the duck-billed platypus, made of pliable horny material; (2) turtle's beak with hard, horny edges; (3) vulture's beak which can crack bones like rib shears in the hand of the surgeon; (4) giant beak of the pelican with expansible sac of skin. The ruff (5) uses its beak to pick up small worms and seeds from the ground as though with tweezers.

scrapers and chewers; they scrape outside the mouth and chew in the mouth. For example, the ruminants steady the grass with the incisors in their lower jaws, seize hold of it with their big, muscular tongues, which are covered with hard, pointed papillae, and tear it out with a circular movement. There are also many combinations of gulpers and chewers or gulpers and scrapers. When a man eats bread he is a chewer, and when he swallows an oyster he is a gulper!

Many creatures make no attempt to break up large pieces of food but instead take only tiny particles. A specific form of this kind of eating is sucking. Other special devices are required for this in addition to the original sucking mechanism. These licking apparatuses take many different forms and can be extremely complex. For example, many mammals, such as the little tarsipes of Australia, a shrew-like phalanger, have 'licking tongues'. This Australian

116

mammal has a long tongue which can be stuck out for a considerable distance. It is toothed at the edges and covered with short hairs, which unite at the end in a short 'paint brush'. In addition, the lips form flaps of skin, whose task it is to convert the open mouth into a kind of suction pump, and with the help of this pump the creature sucks up insects and honey from flowers.

Licking and sucking mechanisms have indubitably reached their highest stage of development in insects. These mechanisms are used either for the consumption of pollen, sap and nectar, by a mixture of chewing and licking, as in the case of many beetles and ants, or else simply for licking and sucking up nutritive fluids, as in the case of numerous species of flies.

To penetrate to plant juices, blood, or lymph, and start the act of sucking, creatures often have to break through protective coverings, either by pricking or sawing. All kinds of pricking devices have been developed in land creatures. One has only to think of many primitive insects, of lice, all the plant suckers, fleas, and stinging flies. Some kinds of lice can pierce even the woody parts of plants; with the aid of very long prickly bristles they bore through thick layers of bark until they reach the cells full of sap. To prevent trickles of blood choking the sucking mechanism, mites and stinging insects, which feed in such large quantities on land mammals, have developed an 'anti-coagulant' in their gland cells; in addition, another substance dilates the capillaries and the smallest little veins, thus necessarily producing a stronger flow of blood. Within twenty minutes ticks can suck in five times their own weight in blood.

The abundance of arrangements and capacities which creatures have developed in order to procure and consume food is really astounding; the variety is so great that a complete survey is impossible. It is precisely the contrasts in ability and equipment that enable all the innumerable species to survive.

ENDLESS CHAIN OF FOOD

The separate members of the terrestrial community form a sort of pyramid so far as their need for food is concerned: the lowest stage is formed by the plants, on which the herbivores live; these serve in turn as food for the carnivores. Nor should we forget the nutritional chain in which plant or animal waste provides the basic nourishment for soil organisms, which themselves form the food of other species. Everything living always serves as food for other living things.

In the soil itself the 'producers' retire into the background. Autotrophic plants, such as the edaphic algae, are present only on the surface and in the topmost layers; here they can be of some importance as a source of food to individual inhabitants of the soil. A rôle which is fundamentally more important to the ground and the life in it is played by the earth's covering of vegetation. It provides organic remains as a basic source of food for soil organisms, and it also provides the raw material of humus.

A large number of the inhabitants of the soil work as 'consumers' on the animal and vegetable remains, transforming them physically and chemically. Parallel to this activity, processes of decay go on in the soil, furthered for the most part by the bacteria and fungi which are active as 'reducers', and thus carry out the important task of mineralizing the organic material in the soil. The activity of these 'reducers' is of decisive importance to plants, which can only make use of mineral substances when they have been set free by the 'reducers'. It is no less important that the mineral substances should be as easily available as possible to the roots of plants, and this is brought about by their incorporation in humus, the formation and physical distribution of which is predominantly the work of the 'consumers'. The organic communities of healthy soils are perfectly balanced; their activities fit harmoniously into the whole metabolic cycle of the soil.

The more abundantly populated and many-sided a habitat is, the more manifold are the nutritional links and mutual relations—step by step the whole structure of a biocoenosis can be traced, from any one of a number of different points of view. We can consider the differing positions in the living community of the creatures which eat plants, animals, or waste products, or of those which provide food for many others; that is, either the middle links or the end links of nutritional chains. Or we can look at communities that live together, inside the ground or on its surface, and so forth.

The following brief examples from desert, steppe, and forest will help to illustrate the nutritional chain with which we are concerned at the moment. In the desert, food is not easy to obtain. The hunters and gatherers come off best. Among the hunters are most of the reptiles, the ground beetles, the giant millipedes, and the spiders. Thorough investigations of the contents of desert reptiles' stomachs have yielded informative results. For example, an analysis of the contents of certain lizards' stomachs produced these figures: about 30 per cent butterfly caterpillars, 18 per cent beetle larvae, 13 per cent locusts, 10 per cent black beetles, 6 per cent bugs, and just under 4 per cent spiders. Comparable figures for rattlesnakes were almost 40 per cent reptiles, over 20 per cent locusts, and about 15 per cent carrion beetles. The principal gatherers are the rodents such as mice, hares, ground squirrels, pouched mice, and jumping mice (jerboas); they eat seeds and insects. Ants carry home grains of seed; the honeypot ants store supplies of honey for months at a time in their crops as a precaution against times when food and water are short.

Every stone, every hole in the ground, every tuft of grass in the desert can become a home and centre of activity for bugs, cicadas, and locusts, which serve as food for reptiles and birds. Mice and

Poisonous centipede (Scolopender) *from Indonesia.*

ground squirrels burrow in the earth, and in the holes which they make horned vipers, geckos, and black beetles find refuge.

On the steppe or savannah, the prevalent herbivorous small creatures are grasshoppers, bugs, crickets and seed-gathering ants, which in turn serve as food not only for reptiles but often also for frogs, which in summer emerge from small pools and populate the steppe in large numbers. Voles and other small rodents form the basic food of predatory mammals and snakes.

The luxuriance and variety of life in the tropical rain forest is reflected in the food balance of the animal world. Snakes, lizards, centipedes, spiders, and earthworms are distinguished here as nowhere else by their giant size, and the same is also true of insects.

The number of herbivorous creatures in the tropical rain forest is immense, from rodents down to insects, which are kept in check by birds, reptiles, spiders, scorpions, predatory beetles and bugs, and ants like the driver ant. Ant-bears and ant-eaters feed exclusively on the legions of ants and termites.

119

The food relationships in the deciduous forests of Northern Europe are no less complex and various. Deer, foxes, martens, mice, shrews, and moles are the principal animals concerned; in the forests of North America there are also the opossum, the racoon, and the skunk. The layers of vegetation provide food for a vast number of herbivorous small creatures, and indirectly for the carnivores dependent on the latter. There are not so many spiders and ants in deciduous forests as there are in coniferous ones, but they are still fairly numerous in species and in numbers of individuals. The ground vegetation, which stays moist for a long time, and the plentiful supply of fungi, algae, and lichens enable snails to thrive and multiply. Felled or fallen tree trunks, rotting boughs, mushrooms, and mossy turf have their own fauna. Birds' nests built on the ground, and above all the burrows of the small mammals, are full of parasites and 'commensals', mainly in the form of mice and diptera.

7 *Varying Conditions of Life*

ARTIFICIAL LANDSCAPE—ARTIFICIAL DESERT

Many artificial habitats betray surprising similarities with natural regions; man-made grassland can support animals of the steppe, rice fields can be inhabited by the creatures of the marsh, gardens and parks attract woodland creatures, cellars can have genuine cave dwellers in them, and the outside walls of houses can be inhabited by creatures originally at home in crevices in the rock. But on the whole the activity of man has created new living spaces and new conditions of life, which for living things, especially animals, mean enforced adjustments and often considerable changes in behaviour. During the course of his history man has to an increasing extent transformed wild nature into an artificial landscape. Some thickly populated regions have been so thoroughly remoulded that every trace of natural conditions has been well nigh eradicated.

The first point of attack is always the vegetation. Economic man has remodelled the plant world. Large expanses are covered with a uniform, monotonous vegetation—ploughland, meadow, or specially planted and tended forests, which have been described with some justification as 'wood factories'. To the three great original kinds of vegetation—forest, grassland (steppe), and wilderness (desert)—man has added a fourth, fertile land, and this fertile land (arable, pasture, and orchard) is continually expanding at the expense of the other kinds. The consequences—hastened erosion, the production of steppe and naked rock, storm disasters, and plagues of pests—could have been largely avoided by a better knowledge of ecology. The unrestrained clearance of forests, the burning of prairies, which once provided food and shelter for millions of creatures large and small, the draining of marshes and bogs, over-intensive grazing, the regulation of rivers and the construction of huge dams, the destruction of flora and fauna, and other similar activities have all brought with them unsuspected, and often certainly undesired, results which have radically altered the surface of the earth and extensively damaged its productive capacity.

Parts of the U.S.A., the Mediterranean lands, and the cradles of civilization in Asia and Central America have at one time or another been thickly populated and subject to intensive human intervention; as a result, large stretches of them have by now become barren wildernesses, and within the area tamed by man only small patches of forest remain.

This is what the physicist Plotnikow writes about the drying out of the land in the Volga region: "An enormous drying process has been completed before my eyes in the Volga region. About 100 years ago the banks of the Volga were covered with thick forest and the stream was broad and powerful. About 45 years ago, when I travelled the length of the Volga as a schoolboy, the banks were already bare and the grassy steppe half dried up. Now, a few years ago, it was reported that because of silting-up and lack of water the steamers could not operate for some time and even the level of the Caspian Sea had sunk considerably. A desert is coming into being, a desert that will soon join the Gobi and Shano deserts and deprive ten to twenty million people of their bread."

The American geologist Tugwell describes the drying-up process in the mountains and the Mississippi in these words: "In years gone by we were always hearing of the advance of the dried-up zone on the eastern slopes of the Rocky Mountains. Where there were once green meadows and green trees there is today nothing more than a great sandy desert; not even birds of prey circle over it, for they can find nothing to catch there. Both men and animals have withdrawn from the area. Men stripped the land of its turf in order to grow crops on the sand beneath. But the spring and autumn storms first dried the soil and then loosened it. The soil was no longer moist and fertile; it had become sand. And this sand began its travels, always towards the coast, advancing slowly but unceasingly." On the basis of his geographical and climatological studies, Tugwell prophesies that in 300 years' time the Middle West of America will all have turned into sand, the Mississippi will have contracted to a small river, completely dry at places in its upper reaches, and in St Louis the only remains of its present skyscrapers will be a tangle of rusty masts and iron skeletons.

A classic example of the desolation created by deforestation is the Karst region which runs through part of Istria and stretches along the Adriatic to the valley of the Drin. These heights might almost be part of a lunar landscape. There are only two colours here: the blue of the sky and the sea, and the blinding white of the rocks. There is no trace of woodland or meadow, cornfield or orchard. A sinister

Habitats in the Forest of Northern Europe.

1. Bird's nest.
2. Badger's burrow.
3. Ant hill.
4. Cushion of moss.
5. Fungi.
6. Tree stump.
7. Excrement.
8. Carrion.
9. Stones.
10. Individual plants.
11. Broken boughs.
12. Leaves.
13. Branch.
14. Hollow of a tree.
15. Bark.
16. Root.

silence broods over the landscape: no birds sing, no insects hum; all is deathly quiet. Even on the ground it is clear how life has to struggle for its rights; stunted bushes hide in hollows and brightly flowering herbs spring from the cracks between the rocks. Lizards dart like greenish-gold flashes of lightning over the stones, and between the stones are curious beetles and spiders.

Even in the Karst district a kind of farming goes on. In the fields of boulders there are numerous, often deep, roundish holes, which look like small craters. The few streams and rivers of the region

123

usually disappear into these funnels, which are called dolines and form the whole wealth of the region. The rain washes together what little soil there is into these hollows (or dolines), and if it is not enough the farmer plays his part and carries the soil in sacks on his back from little crevices to his dolines. In these round hollows, which are often no more extensive than a big room, he carries on his miserable husbandry.

In spite of the relatively short period of vegetation, fields too display specific living communities with far-reaching relationships; this is true of the surface of the ground, of the vegetation, and of the edaphon. Fundamentally, these communities do not differ very much from natural communities. The creatures that live in the fields react to human interference in widely varying ways. Some stay where they are and take no notice of the changes of vegetation occasioned in successive years by the rotation of crops. These groups of creatures form the fixed basis of an arable community, while those which appear and disappear with the various different crops form the migratory part.

The connections between local climate, nature of the soil and crop, intensity of the various kinds of human intervention—sowing, harrowing, harvesting, ploughing, and so on—and variations in the above-ground communities are quite unmistakable. Soil and crop produce a characteristic climate which to a large extent gives its own stamp to the animal life. Heat, moisture, light, and wind all naturally vary according to the direction, density, and height of the vegetation. Corn, with its long stalk, lets more light and sun reach the ground than root crops or clover. In a field of corn the force of the wind is checked some distance above the ground; in a field of root crops it reaches right to the surface of the ground.

Creatures which prefer the cool shade and a high degree of moisture in the air find the most suitable conditions in the sheltered furrows of a cabbage field, with their subdued light. But the nature of the soil is also of considerable importance to the creatures which live on the surface. Fields of sandy soil are populated by organisms which do not mind a warm, dry environment and which are otherwise normally found on sandy heaths, dunes, and bare, sandy sections of river banks; on the other hand, loam and clay soils show certain affinities in their fauna with the virgin grasslands of the steppe.

The surface fauna of fields is usually distinguished by great uniformity, for cultivated plants with their thicker foliage form an obstacle to the wide distribution of the bigger arthropods, while on the other hand slugs, as a result of the moister micro-climate near the ground, find conditions very favourable.

The absence of a layer of rotting vegetation or any similar shelter makes wintering in fields exceptionally difficult. Any creature exposed to the weather when the land is bare must possess great resistance to cold, as the beetles do. So far as vertebrates are concerned, they often have difficulty in finding places where they can rest and breed undisturbed for any length of time.

The relative poverty of fields, especially in comparison with grassland, is perhaps most striking in the realm of the edaphon, where the

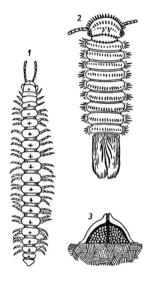

Millipedes. 1. Strongylosoma.
2. Polyxenus.
3. *The egg-bell of a Julus millipede, made of earth and dung (cross-section).*

quantity of organisms fluctuates considerably from one place to another, especially when one compares light with heavy arable land. The number of earthworms, millipedes, and certain insect larvae drops particularly steeply in sandy soil. It is clear from quantitative experiments carried out by the latest methods that on an average a field has three times fewer earthworms, five times fewer threadworms, up to six times fewer mites and simple insects, and ten times fewer small worms than grassland.

Special factors and micro-climatic conditions, not to mention farm operations, normally lead to quite considerable fluctuations in the numbers of edaphic organisms. Most organisms such as earthworms, millipedes, and insect larvae are usually at their maximum in spring and autumn; but the precise moment can naturally vary according to the time when cultivation of the fields ends and when the ground begins to be sheltered by the growing plants.

In arable land, as in all soils, the rhizosphere is the main living space. However, earthworms very often live at greater depths and can penetrate over 30 inches into the ground. Outside Central Europe the vertical distribution of the edaphic creatures can be very different. On newly tilled soil to the east of the Aral Sea, Russian scientists found millipedes 32 to 36 inches down, earthworms at depths of 20 inches, and small worms at depths of 8 to 12 inches. Even at depths of 40 inches beetle larvae and various primitive insects were discovered, but these were exceptional instances.

By clearing forests and draining marshes and bogs, or by utilizing steppe and alpine slopes, man has created grassland and in many cases has preserved it by appropriate draining measures, and by mowing, grazing, and manuring it. Since man neither destroys the natural structure of the soil nor takes away an excessively high proportion of the organic substances produced, the activities of 'producers','consumers', and 'reducers' remain fairly well balanced in grassland. The very circumstance that the natural structure of the soil is not altered means that life above and below ground is rich and varied.

For grassland creatures the most important factors are humidity, aeration of the soil, and organic content; in addition there is the acidity of the soil, which influences fungi in particular but is only of subordinate importance to the edaphic organisms, including earthworms. A characteristic of meadowland is the thick tangle of roots running through the top layers of soil, and the permanent existence of a substantial proportion of crumbly soil produces a large volume of pores, on which the looseness of old turf is based. Unlike arable land, which is continually being re-tilled, this kind of ground provides an extensive living space for organisms, and this space is continually being enlarged by the tiny creatures themselves. They eat dead roots and fill with their own bodies the channels which the roots occupied, thus keeping them in being. An essential rôle is played by the unimaginably numerous and varied fungi; they clothe all the crevices and hollows in the soil with their fine, slimy mycelium, which forms a branching network of very thin threads. It is precisely this microscopically fine binding of the soil that produces the best kind of crumbly consistency and in conjunction with the roots of the higher plants prevents rainwater turning the top of the soil into mud.

126

All the organisms of meadowland, both above and below ground, are united in a close-knit structure, which ranges from bacteria and infusoria, via simple insects, mites, and beetles, together with their parasites, via predatory spiders and plant-sucking cicadas, bugs, and caterpillars, right up to field mice. These field mice, when they are present in large numbers, can decisively alter the character of the vegetation and consequently the whole basis of life of numerous tiny creatures which live on the surface of the ground and inside it. The mice lay bare, loosen up, and manure the ground; this allows a host of weeds to spring up, which in turn support a whole range of snails, spiders, beetles, and herbivorous insects.

Many universal pests of cultivated land, such as cockchafer grubs, wireworms, crane-fly larvae, and ploughland snails, occur first and foremost in grassland. It is here that the eggs are laid from preference, since the thick covering of vegetation with its matted mass of roots and the high moisture content of the upper layers of soil offer the best conditions for the development of the early stages of these organisms. In addition, purely nutritional factors also come into play, in so far as the grubs of these pests feed on humus when they first hatch out. They use decayed vegetable matter or ground water containing organic substances in solution and only turn to living roots later on.

If we compare edaphic conditions in grassland with those prevailing in cultivated land throughout the course of the year, the manifold connections between the vegetation and the life of the soil become clear at once. The number of organisms in grassland follows a uniform curve determined by the seasons, while in arable land this curve is sharply interrupted by every agricultural operation and even by the harvest itself.

If the turf is broken up, the whole tangle of roots dies. The volume of pores is reduced more and more, the structure of the soil gradually deteriorates, and this reduces the number of individual organisms and species of organisms which it can support. When the ground is ploughed up, the organisms in the soil have to re-orientate themselves completely and adapt themselves to largely different conditions, not least to a different annual rhythm. It then becomes quite evident that conditions for the edaphon are in many respects more favourable in meadowland than in ploughland. The far greater density of roots in meadowland means a valuable reserve of food for the soil organisms and also contributes considerably to the enlargement of the volume of pores and hence to the whole living space.

Moreover, the permanent covering of vegetation guarantees a very well-balanced ground climate without extreme contrasts in temperature or fluctuations in humidity.

The reduction in the life of the soil caused by the breaking-up of the turf can be counterbalanced to some extent by cultivation and by the use of varied fertilizers, so that if the soil is properly tended and utilized it does not become compressed. But the soil life of newly laid-down grassland always shows the characteristics of ploughland, and can only re-acquire those of meadowland by a process of development that takes many years. The lack of fermenting agents reduces the number of soil organisms and necessarily cripples the activity of the soil as a whole.

The domain of human settlements and buildings, which has been christened 'man-made desert', as opposed to the less fundamentally altered 'man-made steppe', has its own special climatic conditions.

The temperatures of towns tend to be higher; severe fluctuations are levelled out by the micro-climate prevailing in the houses. However, the relative humidity of the air is less than it is in the surrounding countryside; smoke and soot create a layer of haze that absorbs much of the direct sunshine—all in all, the result is a dry, warmer climate. This means that conditions in the immediate neighbourhood of buildings are favourable to insects, which for the most part betray unmistakable links with life in the open country. This is also true of rats, and mice, spiders, mites, isopods, and snails; in many cases the place of origin is clearly the forest, with its tree trunks, animal nests, and fungi. Rats and mice have been attracted to the neighbourhood of man by the impulse to live in small holes and not least by the profusion of food.

In hot regions termites tunnel unseen into houses, usually by night, for they like a certain amount of moisture and need it, too, since their soft hindquarters, which have little chitin on them, cannot tolerate too much heat or sunshine. They eat away the inside of beams, posts, and furniture without doing the slightest damage to the surface. A thin outside layer remains in place, until suddenly the objects concerned collapse and change at a touch into a heap of crumbly wood.

The beech woods of Northern Europe belong to the deciduous forest of the temperate zone. The light-hungry vegetation at ground level has to depend on the few rays of sunlight that reach it through the roof of leaves. (Photo: Harald Doering.)

Other injurious inhabitants of dry wood are the wood block beetle, the shot borer, and above all the death watch beetle. Here we should also mention the insects which occur in damp wood covered with fungus, especially at the base of fence posts and telegraph poles; foremost among them are the weevils, which originally belonged to the regular fauna of the forest. Their tunnels are often used as nesting places by wasps, bees, earwigs, flour beetles, and bacon beetles.

For breaking down cell walls, and also for proteins and vitamins, most wood-inhabiting insects rely on symbiotic micro-organisms or fungi that grow in wood. In the cracks and crevices of walls, and above all at their bases, isopods, earwigs, mites, and various kinds of fungi find favourable conditions, while the shafts of subterranean tunnels provide hiding places for cockroaches and ants.

The typical flora and fauna of cellars are adapted to a life in the darkness or semi-darkness; they show certain affinities with the flora and fauna of caves. There are fewer simple insects in bunkers and cellars than there are in caves; beetles play the predominant rôle— mainly rove beetles, brass beetles, and black beetles. Alongside them live isopods, earwigs, predatory fungus-midge larvae, the cellar leaf louse, and the cellar moth, never yet found outside this domain. The basic food of all these creatures consists of fungi and algae, which in addition largely regulate the humidity. During the daytime damp, dark corners provide a hiding place for the cellar snail, which in turn is hunted by the natterjack.

The slag heaps and refuse heaps on the outskirts of towns and villages, and vacant sites in towns, also form an important type of man-made habitat. Originally for the most part deficient in vegetation, these localities represent relatively rich sources of food. The plants which grow there in turn provide the basis for a rich fauna. In the early stages of colonization nightshades, notch-weeds, and cruciferous plants predominate; in the later stages leguminous plants and true grasses replace them.

The loose texture of slag and the usually incomplete covering of vegetation results in daily fluctuations of temperature which are greater than those found in fields and show certain parallels with those of dunes. Only in the interior of refuse heaps is the process of

---

The bare, inhospitable Karst in the north-west of Yugoslavia. Wherever man destroys the forest, he creates a desert! (Photo: W. Schmolcke/Bavaria.)

I

decay of the organic materials connected with the marked production of heat: for example, measurements have disclosed a temperature about 110°F to 120°F at a depth of eight inches when the external temperature was about 55°F.

HIDDEN HABITATS

The most varied combinations of species can appear on a piece of carrion, depending on the surroundings. They form an unstable micro-community, very much at the mercy of weather conditions. This community goes through an exceptionally swift succession of phases. First of all, anaerobic bacteria appear inside the corpse.

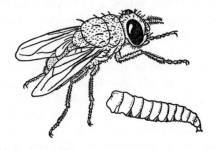

Housefly (Musca domestica) *and its larva.*

Simultaneously with this bacterial dissolution from within comes destruction from without by flies, which have been attracted by the smell of decay and lay their eggs. The intensive activity of the larvae which emerge from the eggs considerably checks the bacterial processes, either because the larvae suck up the substances liquified by the bacteria or because secretions in the skin of the larvae kill the bacteria. The next stage in the process of disintegration is a mass development of the unicellular creatures present in the ground as cysts or otherwise. First come infusoria, whip algae, and various amoebas, but threadworms, carrion beetles, and dung beetles also appear. There are often mites clinging to their chitin or their limbs.

Other competitors which soon arrive are burying beetles, attracted from afar by their fine sense of smell. These creatures try instinctively to bury animal corpses and to lay their eggs in them, and they exert themselves to accomplish this task as quickly as possible. In the ground corpses are protected not only from the air but also from high temperatures, which hasten decay considerably. Usually several beetles work together, removing the soil from underneath the corpse, so that it sinks down; they also pull it down. Often they have to bury a body in ground covered with grass; in such cases, with great 'instinctive skill' they bite through the blades and roots that hinder them.

As soon as decomposition sets in, bacon beetles and simple insects, particularly springtails, appear on the scene. As the corpse dries out they are joined by certain beetles, cheese fly larvae, with their striking ability to jump, and numerous mites, until only bones, hair, or feathers are left. The work of destruction is finally completed by certain species of beetles, fur moths, or the caterpillars of the pyralis moth.

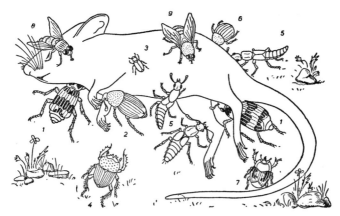

Carrion insects on a dead field mouse. 1. *Burying beetle.* 2. *Black carrion beetle.* 3. *Bacon beetle.* 4. *African pill roller.* 5. *Rove beetle.* 6. *Short beetle.* 7. *Forest dung beetle.* 8. *Grey blowfly.* 9. *Bluebottle.*

Similar temporary centres of activity are formed by excrement, where dependence on swiftly changing physical conditions permits only inhabitants which develop quickly. The fluctuations of temperature in the layer of air next to the ground in open positions causes considerable variations of heat in the excrement, and these have a marked effect on the succession of inhabitants. In addition, a large proportion of the excremental organisms, and particularly of the animals taking part in the process of destruction, often seem to be very demanding in the matter of environmental conditions; this is the only way in which we can explain the specific biocœnoses of cowpats, of horse and sheep dung, of the protein-rich droppings of beasts of prey, or of the excrement of deer and hares. In cattle dung, up to a fifth of the dry material consists of bacteria, while in the case of dogs the figure is hardly ten per cent and in that of rabbits not more than two per cent.

On cowpats, whose fauna is best known, the first arrivals are usually horse flies, which come to lay their eggs on the still fresh excrement. They are followed by dung flies, hover flies and, rather surprisingly, terrestrial members of the great water-beetle family, which move about in the still semi-liquid dung. Their activity helps ventilation and hastens the natural drying-out process. Only now do dung beetles appear on the scene; they bore through the dung into the ground, where they lay their eggs.

In the system of tunnels subsequently produced by the activity of flies and beetles—tunnels which are prevented from drying up by the crust which has meanwhile formed on the surface—fungi and layers of yeast and bacteria develop; it is they which produce the dark brown colour inside and the characteristic smell. In the last stage of the process of decay and drying out, simple insects, click beetle larvae, and earthworms appear. Besides the exclusively coprophagous inhabitants of these small habitats, predatory ground beetles and fly maggots are to be found there. The dung-inhabiting beetles carry in on their bodies threadworms, which feed on fungi and bacteria, and also predatory mites, which use this means of transport to reach excrement.

Cattle dung takes a relatively long time to dry, and this usually allows the leaf beetles, dung beetles, mites, and fly larvae which live there to complete their development undisturbed, but the creatures that tackle horse dung, which can decay into a dry mass of threads in two weeks, must either produce larvae that develop very quickly— like the dung beetle, for example—or else bury a considerable quantity of dung in the ground, like the dor beetles. The situation is much the same with the swiftly drying droppings of smaller animals such as sheep or rabbits; they are mostly buried by beetles.

Fallen tree trunks and stumps contain characteristic societies, whose composition is very largely determined by local conditions such as climate, season, and the nature of the wood. Of primary importance for the start of the colonization, and therefore of the process of disintegration, is the condition of the tree when it fell or was cut down. If it falls when the sap is rising all kinds of wood insects are attracted to it, especially black beetles, tick beetles, and weevils. The flowing sap also attracts dung beetles, stag beetles, and innumerable flies. Yeast spores blow on to the sap and make it ferment, and in the fermenting sap threadworms, mites, and the larvae of beetles and snipe flies develop in large numbers. But except for the insects which lay their eggs in the wood all these creatures are of little importance so far as the decomposition of the wood is concerned.

On the other hand, if the tree is felled in the late autumn, it can change so much during the course of the winter that by the spring occupation by wood-demolishing organisms can start quite normally. The first occupants of the trunk—for example, weevils, which begin to gnaw on the borderline where bark meets wood, and pin hole beetles, which bring with them ambrosia fungi that proliferate in the passages gnawed by the larvae and serve as food for them—do not find sufficiently damp hiding places in the bark, which is breaking up through dryness. Only insects which can tolerate very dry conditions can go on living; this means in the first instance wood wasps, *Buprestis* beetles, and death-watch beetles, which convert a large part of the fallen wood into fine sawdust. Only when the stump and its surroundings have been thoroughly moistened again are conditions right for further decomposition by other organisms.

The destruction of the wood is now taken in hand from two directions: from outside, and from the ground, by organisms which penetrate the roots and lower parts of the trunk. The cracks and splits in the wood, which are caused by the drying-out process and which hold the moisture for a long time after rain, are occupied mainly by mites, ringworms, and threadworms, but also by springtails, which lay their eggs in them, and by predatory ground beetles, dwarf spiders, and smooth-bellied spiders. More and more fungi penetrate, and fungoid wood of this sort is gnawed with enjoyment by the larvae of prickly beetles. Enemies of these larvae also appear on the scene without warning: robber flies, certain moth caterpillars, and click beetle larvae.

The outside and top of the stump are covered not only with fungi but also with layers of algae, which are eaten by slugs. The slugs' excrement is in turn important for the further settlement and decomposition of the trunk, because it dries out relatively slowly and forms 'manured' spots where moss and lichen can begin to grow. The cushions of moss and lichen harbour a specific micro-community, consisting of wheel and bear animals, threadworms, and mites. This community has, it is true, no direct effect on the disintegration of the wood, but makes an indirect contribution to it. Because of its capacity for storing water for quite a long time, this living space makes the wood-consuming organisms largely independent of brief climatic fluctuations and thus furthers their development.

As soon as the layers of moss and lichen loosen up, little bristle-worms, threadworms, and mites make their way inward through the passages bored by the wood beetles and click beetles and multiply abundantly inside the tree stump, making a system of cavities and cracks. Through the activity of all these creatures—together with the multitude of micro-organisms—the stump rots away from the top and the wood is transformed into a mass of decaying matter.

The progressively decomposing stump becomes a welcome shelter for many creatures in dry weather and during the winter. Inside the still moist envelope the process of decay goes on unhindered, with isopods playing a particularly conspicuous part. In the continually softening mass of the stump—this stage is usually reached after eight to ten years—ground beetles, wasps, and other insects find a resting place, usually pursued by wolf spiders and jumping spiders, predatory beetles, and fly larvae (wood flies). When the stump's walls, which have been growing thinner and thinner, finally cave in, the last phase in the process of decay has been reached. The last survivors of the wood-consuming fauna—fire beetles, click beetles, isopods, millipedes, and earthworms—then gradually return to their normal life in the ground.

The variety of all these phenomena and processes makes it quite clear what an important role the edaphic organisms of a miniature community of this sort play in a very narrow space. The inconspicuous amoebas, springtails, wheel and bear animals, mites, algae, infusoria, and bacteria, which live in a tangled web of fungus, the innumerable worms, millipedes, rock creepers, and other insects which play such a decisive part in the transformation of cellulose in the forest, all create out of wood, foliage and needles, reeds, pods and spores the valuable preparatory stages of humus, from which humus itself is later formed.

The community of organisms living under a stone is very curious. Most of the species concerned show great sensitivity to brightness and dryness, but few of them are capable of evading external dangers by quickly digging themselves in. Some are tied to living under stones and occur only seldom on the surface of the ground or inside it when there are no stones at hand. In contrast to these genuine 'hypolithic' species, other creatures make use of stones only as places of refuge in bad weather or at unfavourable times of day and do not as a rule even look for food under them. The chief 'stone dwellers' are ants and isopods; others are millipedes, spiders, ground beetles, earthworms, snails, and lizards. The population is highest in autumn, when spiders, rove beetles and other beetles are looking for a home for the winter.

It is interesting to note that on the coasts of northern Europe there lives a bird which seeks its food on the shore and on rocks and in the process turns over smallish stones and dines on the worms and tender molluscs hiding underneath. It is a species of plover with rather short legs; known as the stone curlew, it has a conical, bent-up beak, which is very helpful when it comes to turning over stones.

Very varied miniature biocœnoses are found under mushrooms, for besides food they also provide shelter from the rain and the rays of the sun. The species found under mushrooms and toadstools

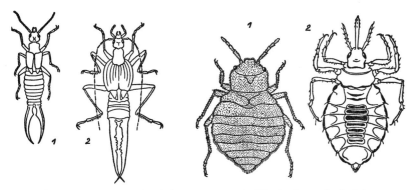

Left: Earwigs. 1. *Male of the common earwig* (Forficula auricularia). 2. *Tropical earwig* (Chelisochella)—*Right: Surface parasites. Just as sand martins have their own species of bug* (Oeciacus, 1), *so the* Haematomyzus *louse* (2) *lives on the skin of the elephant.*

vary considerably according to the site; the most abundant animal life is found under fungi growing amid the undergrowth of damp woodland. Hosts of primitive insects and rove beetles occur, as well as isopods, which prefer old, decaying fungi, and slugs, which like to eat the fungi. Predatory mites, pseudo-scorpions, and earwigs are also found in these spots. In the decomposition of old, decaying fungi, each individual place has its own creatures: slugs and insects make the first swiftly decaying holes in the edges; in the second phase rove beetles are dominant; and later on the larvae of midges and flies appear upon the scene, until the fungus collapses into a rotten, fluid mass, which chiefly attracts dung beetles.

A characteristic fauna and micro-flora lives in the ubiquitous moss cushions, which are characterized by frequent and severe changes of living conditions. Sometimes sunshine and wind make them very dry; the organisms can avoid this by withdrawing deeper into the ground. On the other hand, the spongy nature of the cushions, which can hold a good deal of water, make it essential for their guests to be able to tolerate very wet conditions for some time. These communities consist for the most part of simple insects, moss mites, and often the larvae of land midges, but occasionally isopods, beetles, spiders, and earthworms are also found in moss.

Heaps of hay and straw affect the climate of the layer of air next to the ground. According to the height of the heap, various damp zones can be distinguished, and heat-producing processes of decomposition take place. These spots become hiding places for certain concentrations of creatures, especially damp-loving kinds such as frogs, slugs, insect larvae, mould-eating small beetles, simple insects, and mites.

In the dwellings of warm-blooded animals a great variety of creatures is found: flies and beetles, which live on their host's excrement or make do with the remains of its food; flea larvae, fly maggots, dust lice, mites, and isopods, which feed on fungoid nest material and other organic substances; predatory and parasitic species, such as spiders, parasitic wasps, and rove beetles, which live on the other tiny creatures present; and finally true parasites such as blood-sucking bugs, fleas, ticks, and mites.

Bird's nests have their own special tenants, the species varying according to whether the nest is a proper one or a hole in the ground. Many inhabitants of nests find them through their sense of smell; others arrive on their hosts or with the material of the nest.

The underground burrows of badgers, foxes, hamsters, marmots, rabbits, mice, and moles all have their own fauna composed of fleas, mites, beetles, and flies. The lodgers in ants' and termites' nests are just as characteristic. For example, leaf lice and shield lice live with ants, putting their nutritious excrement at the ants' disposal; so do rove beetles and club beetles, whose pleasant-tasting and intoxicating skin secretions are greedily consumed by the ants. The small club beetle is helplessly dependent on its hosts. It has very poor sight and has to be guided by its feelers; it is fed from the ant's crop.

Besides these guests there are other lodgers which find food and warmth in ants' nests but play no further part in them. Some of them are very similar to their hosts, or else so constructed that they are invulnerable to attacks from the ants (armour, speed, similarity

136

to ants, similarity to the material of the nest), but in addition there are hostile lodgers, which live on their hosts' young. Termites' nests, too, contain a considerable number of lodgers. Some of them, such as springtails and silverfish, cannot be caught or attacked because of their small size and their speed. Rove beetles, isopods, and millipedes are also found in termites' nests.

Small expanses of water hold a special biological interest. Many small patches of water, which are liable to dry up for weeks or even months at a time, are produced by violent downpours or storms and can appear in many places: in hollows and holes in the ground, ruts in the road, tree stumps, and so on.

Temperatures stay close to those of the surrounding area. The marked changes in colour usually displayed by periodic pools

Saltwater Pool Fauna
1. Embletonia pallida (*snail*), *real size about* 7 *millimetres.*
2. *Larva and*
3. *Pupa of the* Ephydra, *a wide-mouthed fly, real size up to* 15 *millimetres.*
4. Tanais, *closely related to an isopod, real size* 2 millimetres.

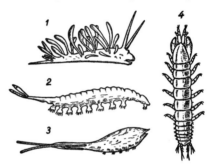

depend mainly on the geological character of the bed, but sometimes they can be traced back to the mass development of lower organisms; red, brown, and green can be caused by flagellates, red and black by other unicellular creatures and tiny crustaceans. Oxygen content is usually fairly high, which is understandable in view of the small depth and relatively large surface area. Even pools extensively polluted with organisms always contain a strikingly large amount of oxygen; this is because the water is very easily aerated. Shallow pools with plenty of algae growing in them, or with a massive quantity of flagellates and similar organisms, are distinguished by a high content of hydrogen sulphide; on the other hand, pools in shady spots—accumulations of ground water in forests, for example, where the ground is covered with leaves—produce mainly hydrogen, ammonia, and carbon dioxide.

Only creatures capable of completing their development in the short time at their disposal or of living through dry periods in resting stages can inhabit these pieces of surface water.

137

Many threadworms and bear animalcules do without any kind of protective element and simply remain in a dormant state with lowered metabolism. Bear animalcules draw in the head, hind part, and extremities, and assume the shape of a small barrel. In this condition the creatures can withstand cold, heat, and lack of oxygen, but not always ultra-violet rays. Many organisms that live in periodic pools guard against the danger of complete drying-out by creeping into the mud or into the ground. Not only snails, mussels, worms, and insect larvae, but also sticklebacks and young newts can survive periods of drought, a phenomenon that can be observed again and again in the pools formed by rivers which overflow their banks.

RHYTHM OF LIFE

Organisms' periods of activity and rest often follow a daily rhythm. Light, temperature, and humidity vary throughout the day, and the rhythm of day and night differs from one landscape or climatic region to another. For example, equatorial deserts have days and nights of approximately equal length all through the year, in contrast to sub-polar regions, where typical nocturnal creatures are rarer. In the northern tundra the fauna has no definite day and night rhythms.

Some rodents become active exclusively at night; a good example is the little white-footed mouse of the North American forests. Most ground beetles only come out of their hiding places at dusk; earthworms, many snails, most millipedes, predatory spiders, and isopods without a top layer of chitin have a completely or predominantly nocturnal mode of life. But no creatures can be categorically described as diurnal or nocturnal, for instinctive behaviour governed by the rhythm of day and night is sometimes disturbed and altered by environmental factors. In its natural state the brown rat is decidedly a twilight animal, active on waste ground, the banks of ditches, and similar spots in early morning and soon after sunset. In the immediate neighbourhood of human habitations, the disturbing proximity of man, the noise of the traffic and the daily legacy of food cause a shift of activity to the nocturnal hours. Certain North American carrion beetles stay hidden on warm, dry nights, and in the summer are active only on cool, damp nights. In the tropical rain forest many cicadas chirp during violent storms which change day into night and stop again as soon as the sun comes from behind the clouds. Most small rodents such as mice, ground squirrels, and

138

mole-rats have short alternating periods of rest and activity during the course of each twenty-four hours, even if the bulk of their activity falls in the morning and evening hours.

The close connections between daily rhythm on the one hand and light, heat, and humidity of the air on the other are unmistakable. Many weakly pigmented beetles which only come out into the light at dusk are not protected against the injurious effects of ultra-violet rays. Investigations into the daily rhythm of beetles in open country, in fields, in dunes, and so on have demonstrated that those with a metallic appearance move about in the day, even in the brightest sunshine, while purely nocturnal species have as a rule no reflecting cuticle.

Many arthropods that live in dunes appear on the surface of the sand only when the sun is out and dig themselves in when it sets.

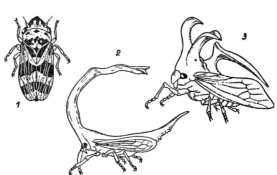

Cicadas
    1. *European cicada* (Aphrodes)
(3 *millimetres*).
    2. *Curiously shaped species from Mexico* (17 *millimetres*).
    3. *Hump-backed cricket from South Africa* (7 *millimetres*).

Many nocturnal mammals, amphibians, and snails in the edges of forests and on the banks of streams need plenty of humidity in the air, and that is why their period of rest ends at nightfall. In the meadows, where the ground warms up slowly and the dew often lasts for a long time, diurnal creatures—especially beetles, cicadas, and grasshoppers—only become active fairly late.

The differences in the daily habits of species with the same mode of life and of feeding result in a biologically significant diminution of the competition for food and thus of the factors of opposition and hostility. This is particularly striking in the case of predatory species, which are kept apart from each other by this temporal isolation. For example, wolf spiders usually search for food in the daytime, while the smooth-bellied and other varieties prefer the night. Much the same is true of many ground beetles that live in the fields.

139

In the tropics all animal and vegetable life is exposed to largely uniform climatic conditions. Life goes on in constantly favourable conditions. It is quite different in the temperate and cool zones with their changing seasons. The rhythm of the year produces changes in light, temperature, and humidity which force organisms to make fairly severe adjustments in their search for food and their efforts to breed and protect themselves against their enemies. On the whole, seasonal alterations in environment, due to seasonal variations in climate, are far more fundamental than daily ones.

For terrestrial organisms, and not least for mammals, the cold season brings an acute food problem. For the herbivorous creatures there is food available, even in winter, in the form of roots, seeds, buds, and so on. Mice and voles make runs and tunnels in the grass underneath the snow in order to reach their sources of food. Shrews hunt for the insects which winter in the ground, and in frost the mole goes deeper for the worms which form its main food. The heaps of earth protruding from the snow testify to its eager digging. When unfavourable weather arrives, many mammals retire to their burrows or hiding places and remain inactive without an actual drop in body temperature; their condition is simply one of deep sleep, in which breathing rate, heart beat, and blood pressure drop to low levels. Since bodily movement is absent metabolism is reduced, and so in consequence is the need for food. In this winter sleep animals consume their usually rich stock of reserve substances. A well-known example is the North American prairie dog; in autumn it becomes unusually fat and can survive long periods of hunger in a state of inactivity and sleep. The European Grimbart badger, too, sometimes stays in its burrow for several weeks at a time during bad weather and sleeps until it is over. Occasionally it comes out for a drink and to look for food.

The winter cold forces the majority of cold-blooded (poikilothermous) animals to cease activity and wait in a state of winter rest. This is because these creatures cannot keep their body temperature at its optimum independently of the temperature of their surroundings. The state of winter rest is characterized by the slowing-down of all vital functions as the body cools down; movement ceases and metabolism is reduced to a minimum.

When the cooler weather arrives in the autumn many snails creep into the ground, under leaves and mould, and withdraw into their shells, closing them up with one or more layers of slime. The European edible snail forms a lid of chalk which covers up the opening in the shell. At suitable spots—on slopes, the edges of ditches, under bushes—these snails dig hollows for themselves in loose soil with the aid of their foot. They lay themselves in these hollows—sometimes covered with particles of earth or leaves—in such a way that the opening of the shell is uppermost and horizontal. Then from the edge of the shell a whitish, chalky fluid is excreted, which quickly hardens and forms a seal. If this 'chalk' lid is removed and the shell left open, the snail inevitably dies in the first frost.

Spiders and millipedes shelter in the ground or under stones or moss. Ground insects winter in every conceivable form, often as egg or chrysalis, but sometimes also as larva or as a mature insect. Most diptera spend the winter as larvae or chrysalises in the earth, in dung or in compost heaps. Ants abandon those parts of their nests which lie above ground and withdraw into deeper sections; whatever happens they remain in their organized societies. Many predatory ants build winter nests in protected spots; these winter nests are often a long distance away from the main nest.

Reptiles seek out quarters in the ground protected against frost and wind, and there they spend the winter in a state of winter rest until the warm days return, when they awake into fresh, active life. Slow-worms like to dig themselves into the ground with the hard tips of their heads and often congregate in subterranean holes. Ring snakes make for dung heaps and compost heaps, where as a result of the process of decomposition the temperature is relatively high.

Naturally the length of this winter rest depends on the weather conditions in any particular year and on the geographical location. In mild Mediterranean districts it may last only two months; in northern lands it can last eight months or more.

A few warm-blooded animals, too, withdraw into hiding places and hibernate, which means a complete readjustment of their whole metabolism. Breathing and heart beat are greatly reduced and the temperature of the outside of the body sinks until it approximates to the temperature of the environment. Even the composition of the blood is altered. The sensitivity of the nervous system is greatly reduced and voluntary defensive movements are no longer possible.

The hibernating animals of Northern Europe include the alpine marmot, the dormouse, the ground squirrel, and the hamster. Of the insect-eating mammals, only the hedgehog hibernates, while the other members of this order—the mole and the shrews—remain lively. Even under deep snow these two creatures find enough insects to feed on.

Recent investigations have shown that the winter sleep is controlled by hormones. The thyroid gland of hibernating mammals shows radical alterations, which indicate a reduced secretion of hormones. Just as there must be a state of inner readiness for normal sleep—namely, real tiredness—so there must be a readiness for winter sleep, caused by internal factors, before the start of hibernation. At the same time the surroundings must have a low temperature; this is the important external factor which triggers off the desire to sleep. The critical temperature differs from one animal to

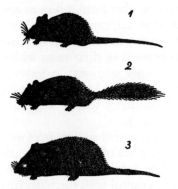

Even mice are an important link in the chain of land animals.
Characteristic kinds of mice:
1. The 'genuine mouse', including the house mouse, the barn mouse and the house rat.
2. The 'sleeping mouse'—e.g. the dormouse.
3. The 'vole' (field mouse, earth mouse).

another; for the hamster it is about 50°F, for the dormouse about 60°F. Above this limit either the animal remains awake or the winter sleep is only very light. As the cold season draws to an end, the readiness for sleep declines, so that when warmer temperatures arrive the animal awakes.

Hibernation occurs in the southern hemisphere as well. The little marsupial dormouse of Australia accumulates such a store of fat for its long sleep that it becomes as round as a ball.

COLONIZATION

A very interesting phenomenon from the biological point of view is colonization, perhaps of originally bare expanses of rock or of newly created volcanic soil.

In the colonization of rock or eroded expanses a rôle that should not be underestimated is played by the soil organisms. Colonization proper can only take place when there is a basis for the formation of humus, a process which goes on most effectively where the rock has weathered—in depressions, cracks, and crevices.

The first inhabitants of apparently quite bare and bald rock faces are microscopically small plants: green algae, diatoms, and, above all, varieties of blue algae. Vast numbers of these decoratively shaped, multicoloured algae live on the surface of the rock, to which they cling by means of a tough, gelatinous substance, forming a thin layer of particles a millimetre thick. The composition of the algae communities, which show little variety of species where conditions are uniform, alters as soon as the degree of moisture, exposure to the sky, or even the acidity of the ground changes.

What particularly characterizes communities of rock algae and distinguishes them from the lower vegetation of forest, field, and

Green algae as colonizers of rock. Above: Gloeocapsa; *below:* Tren-tepohlia, *typical form of 'ink-stroke' vegetation in limestone mountains.*

meadow is the extraordinary way they can survive weeks and even months of drought without suffering damage. In the slime enveloping their cells they retain the drips and trickles of water which periodically run down the rock face. Scarcely anywhere else does the temperature change so quickly and over such a wide range as on rock faces. On calm summer days these rock faces can reach 125°F, while on cold winter mornings they may drop down to sub-zero temperatures. The traces of nutritive salts released from the rock by the water or washed down from vegetation growing higher up are sufficient, in combination with the carbon which they draw from the carbonic acid in the air, to enable the algae to form carbohydrates and proteins, and thus to build up their tissues and keep themselves alive.

Because of their capability for survival algae cover most cliff-faces, whether limestone, granite, slate, or sandstone, with a transparently thin layer, which gives the rock a grey, bluish, or very dark tint and lends it that warm, finely graduated patina which is so pleasant to the eye. The paths preferred (because of the configuration of the rock) by the water that trickles down periodically are emphasized by the so-called 'ink-strokes', the lush, dark-coloured vegetation of the

143

rock algae. The stronger the light to which they are exposed, the more intensively the algae are pigmented. The colour will be blood-red if the rock is acid, but deep violet if it is alkaline.

The 'biological weathering' begun by the algae is carried further by lichens, fungi, and mosses, which are found in infinitely varying forms at very great altitudes. Lichens can flourish on rock whose surface is only very slightly weathered, although they are parched by the sun and exposed to the most extreme conditions. For this reason lichens are found in all climates: on barren sandy soil, on bald rock faces, on the erratically strewn boulders of the plain, and on the steep crags of the mountains. In the Caucasus they grow above 15,000 feet and in the Alps above 9000 feet. It can even be shown that they survived the Ice Ages in the glaciated regions.

Wherever a little humus is formed the lichens are followed at once by moss. Fine threads of moss penetrate the weathering rock, and in the course of time the surface of the rock is broken up and made receptive to the roots of grasses and small forms of vegetation, which soon occupy the chinks.

In the first cushions of moss and grass all kinds of tiny creatures very soon appear—rhizopods, threadworms, wheel and bear animals, and predatory mites. Wasps and bees build their nest of mud in the cracks and crevices, and these are also used by spiders as hiding places in which to lie in ambush for their prey. All these colonizing creatures, whose activities transform the remains of the algae and lichens, can tolerate very dry conditions.

Once the cushions of moss have spread out further and thus assured the retention of a greater quantity of moisture, infusoria, horned mites, and springtails appear on the scene, transported to it by the wind. In the cracks in the rock these creatures deposit their droppings, so that here organic material is built up, which holds the water and makes the conditions for settlement still more favourable. Snails that feed on algae and lichens are particularly active in this direction. In the 'manured' cracks a mixture of organic and inor-ganic particles develops, thanks to the activities of mites, various beetle larvae, millipedes, and earthworms. By mingling humus and loam, these start to form crumbly soil, which in turn permits coloniza-tion by higher plants, grasses, and shrubs. The grasses permit the development of a rich fauna, while the shrubs in their turn enrich the soil with their dead leaves, largely check loss of water by shading the ground, and tap the nutritive elements in deeper cracks with their roots.

The bittern stays stiff and motionless when danger threatens. In this post-like position it merges completely with its surroundings—a perfect piece of teamwork between fear and the instinct to camouflage itself. (Photo: W. Speckmann.)

If we follow the course of colonization on the outskirts of glaciers, we again find the process beginning with algae, which prepare the way for the first mosses, grasses, and cushiony plants. These make life possible for all the little creatures of the surface; simple insects, click beetle larvae, mites, and leaf lice, together with their enemies (ground beetles, spiders, and shepherd spiders). As the transition to grassland gradually takes place, small worms (*Enchytraeidae*) earthworms, beetles, and snails appear on the scene.

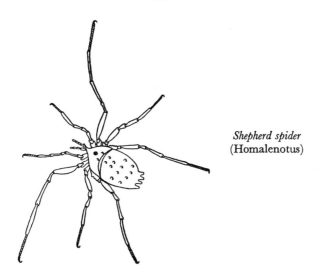

Shepherd spider
(Homalenotus)

Yet another example is the colonization of volcanic soil. The classic instance is the soil of the island of Krakatoa, where after almost eight centuries of volcanic activity there was plenty of room for both plants and animals, but food only for plants. The flora was investigated three years after the great eruption in 1883—long before the first grasses had had time to take root on the hard layer of lava—and an unimaginable wealth of blue algae was found. These algae covered the surface of broken tufa and half-solidified ashes with an almost invisible veil that stretched for miles. The algae were followed by mosses, with their characteristic micro-fauna, and later by isolated grasses and ferns.

Ants in the midst of aphids, which they keep and tend like domestic animals—Ant in 'squirting position' to ward off an attacker. (Photos: H. Doering.)

K

This first vegetation provided food and lodging for a fauna—scanty to begin with—consisting of spiders and insects. With the first trees came the fauna of the forest floor. Fifty years after the eruption, nematodes, web-spinning spiders, and amphibians were still missing. In order of time, the organisms that feed on decaying vegetation were the first to appear; then came the omnivorous and herbivorous creatures; and last of all the predators and parasites.

8 *Environment and Neighbours*

METHODS OF DISTRIBUTION

The air is often full of spores and seeds, winged and wingless, of vegetable and animal organisms. Bacteria and unicellular algae, as spores, make extensive aerial voyages at times up to heights of 30,000 feet, and thermal up-currents carry with them unicellular organisms, mites, spiders, ants, and many other tiny creatures to heights of 12,000 to 15,000 feet. There are tiny species which sometimes develop quite effective adaptations to help them hover; these are often exceptionally resistant to low temperatures and air pressure, and can go on living when they fall back to earth in the rain.

In the southern part of the Indian Ocean lies Kerguelen Island, the home of the sea elephant, the king penguin, and the crested penguin. Its climate is unusually raw and stormy, and the mainland is a long way away. An insect that rises into the air above the island is continually in danger of being carried far out to sea by the strong winds and of perishing there. Thus here the capacity to hover does nothing to preserve or distribute the species, and in fact the insects found on Kerguelen Island—flies, butterflies, and beetles—are all incapable of flight. Their wings are either stumps or completely non-existent. Creatures tied to the ground and incapable of flying or swimming are sometimes carried across the sea on driftwood, and this can result in the colonization of islands which were never connected to any other land.

Land plants are distributed by other agents besides the wind. Fruits and seeds covered with barbed, bristly hairs become attached to passing hairy animals and can cause considerable discomfort. In

South Africa a certain kind of thorn bush bears 'trample burs', which make it feared by man and beast. Livingstone relates how these burs bore into the muzzles of grazing cattle. They cling to the hoofs of springboks, and the poor animals rush about mad with pain until the seed capsule falls off.

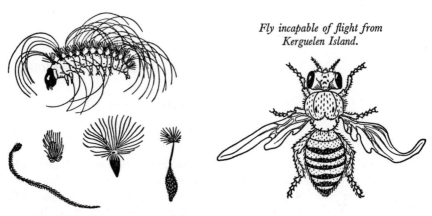

Fly incapable of flight from Kerguelen Island.

Distribution of animals and plants by the wind. Above: Caterpillar of the mud-spinner (Lymantria dispar), *with extremely long hairs as effective enlargement of the surface area. Below: Flying seeds and flying fruits. From left to right: clematis, willow, mountain aster, dandelion.*

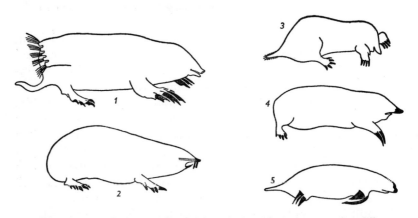

Burrowers: analogies in mode of life and physical structure. 1. Armadillo rat (Bolivia), *insect-eater, 8 inches long. 2. Mole-rat, rodent (south-east Europe), 7 inches long. 3. Mole, insect-eater (Europe), 6 inches long. 4. Golden mole, insect-eater (SouthAfrica), 5 inches long. 5. Pouched mole, marsupial (Australia), 4 inches long. (Partly after Tischler.)*

TEEMING ABUNDANCE OF LIFE

A living community is not merely a collection of organisms; it is a unit in a condition of dynamic equilibrium, governed by precise natural laws, except where man has interfered. The swelling stream of life always comes up against the firmly fixed limits of its living space. Every living community seeks to fill its own living space by over-production of young, whether the living space is a tiny chink in the earth or a vast landscape. If an edaphic infusorian could carry on reproducing itself unhindered in unchanging optimum conditions, the increase in numbers would be so great that in a few years the mass of little organisms would equal the cubic content of our planet.

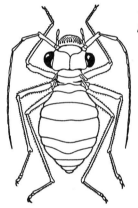

Wingless female of the wood-louse, Mesopsocus.

Gliricola, *a hair worm that lives on rodents. Note the considerably reduced size of the chaetae.*

During the course of its life a queen bee lays 2000 times its own weight in eggs, and a termite queen lays 100 million eggs, yet the numbers of each species remain on the whole much the same. The grass frog, which has many enemies, can produce up to 4000 eggs in a year. In tropical Africa the agate snail, the biggest of the land snails, has today become one of the worst pests. It has been estimated that the progeny of one single female would reach the figure of one million in less than five years if natural enemies did not provide a counterbalance to this reproductive extravagance.

The situation is still more extreme with the parasites, whose main weapon in the struggle for existence is their capacity for multiplication. The cholera bacillus doubles in less than twenty minutes, so that in the course of a day the descendants of one single cell would amount to 1600 trillion! The female maw worm can lay as many as

200,000 eggs a day, and it keeps this up for three-quarters of the year! The tapeworm sheds eight or nine sections every day, and each of them can hold up to 80,000 eggs.

The same is true of the vegetable kingdom. The numbers of spores and seeds needed to make good the losses due to consumption by animals and other causes are enormous. We have only to consider mushroom spores, or the large number of seeds on a tree or in the centre of a poppy.

It is only in recent years, which have brought tremendous improvements in methods of observation, of collecting and of systematic work in general, that we have gained some idea how abundant life in the soil is, both in species and in numbers of individual creatures. One single gram of fertile soil can contain several milliards of bacteria and ray fungi, millions of fungus spores, and hundreds of thousands of fungi, algae, and protozoa. One square yard of ground can support over ten million threadworms, 200,000 mites, 100,000 springtails, tens of thousands of *Enchytraeidae*, wheel and bear animals and many hundreds of millipedes, insect larvae and earthworms. Naturally there are considerable local differences, especially if ploughland is compared with grassland. On an average, there are five times fewer threadworms in a ploughed field than in a meadow of the same size, and eight times fewer insects, ten times fewer *Enchytraeidae* and about three times fewer earthworms. Moisture, aeration and content of organic material are in every case the most important factors in maintaining soil organisms. In addition, the fungus flora is influenced in a particularly striking way by the degree of acidity of the soil.

Noteworthy concentrations of tiny creatures, particularly bacteria, are found in the vicinity of the roots of plants. As a result of the continual excretion of substances vital to them, bacteria grow exceptionally well in the neighbourhood of roots. According to the most modern investigations, carried out with the aid of fluorescence microscopes, the number of bacteria in the soil some distance from the root is between three and six milliards per gram of soil, but in the immediate neighbourhood of the root and on it the number is 50 to 100 times higher, which means that there can be several hundred milliards of germs in one single gram of soil! This concentration of microbes near roots produces in turn an exceptionally strong growth of antibiotic substances and also, through the activity of the microbes, almost certainly of other substances, too, which for their part can gain entrance into the roots.

MAN DISTURBS BALANCE OF NATURE

Human settlement and the cultivation of the soil have thoroughly changed the life of the soil in all its aspects; many organisms can no longer exist, or can exist only in smaller numbers. On the other hand, other species immigrate, are brought in, or occur in larger numbers as a result of the altered conditions. The changes in microclimatic conditions and in living and feeding conditions caused by

Lower fungi in the humus. Diatoms and amoebae can be recognized between the mycelium and the spore-heads of fungi. On the right, a Difflugia *rhizopod, which builds its house out of grains of sand and the shells of dead diatoms.*

the activity of man have affected earthworms as much as snails, spiders, isopods, millipedes, insects, and vertebrates. Even modern motor traffic, with the dust it produces along the sides of the roads and the shaking it gives to the ground—a factor which is by no means without significance from an ecological point of view—is making itself felt more and more. In addition, many creatures—hedgehogs, moles, weasels, snails, beetles, and worms are killed by cars on the main roads. Real biological chain reactions have been started by man in past centuries and decades. Brown and black rats arrived in Australia with the first ships and ousted many small native mammals. The European field mouse displaced the Australian marsupial jumping mouse; and the small snouted marsupial and the marsupial ant eater have today become real rarities. Ships carried rats to Jamaica, where they soon became a serious pest. Then man introduced the mongoose, a small cat-like animal from the East Indies, which set about the rats, and subsequently also lizards, birds that nested on the ground, toads and other creatures. The destruction of their natural enemies meant happy days for the insects, especially shield lice and cockchafer grubs: they devoured man's crops and fruit and he was saddled once again with a pest.

In the course of the last few centuries man has begun to compete more and more everywhere in the world for the plants and creatures that form the food of the bigger species of animals. In numbers, his domestic animals far exceed the big wild animals, which have gradually been pushed further and further back into the dwindling wilds. The area of cultivated land is continually being extended, and in this land man will tolerate, so far as it lies in his power, only those animals which do not significantly reduce the yields of the crops he has sown. Moreover innumerable species of tiny creatures fall victims to this development because they cannot adapt themselves to changes in the plant world. The triumph of technology has destroyed innumerable wild animals and exterminated some species. One has only to think of Australia, where 150 years have sufficed to turn virgin soil into a cultivated landscape; endless forests of eucalyptus have disappeared and vast expanses of savannah have been converted into pasture for cattle. Imported foxes and cats killed off the small marsupials, and the big kangaroos were hunted mercilessly because each of them eats as much as a sheep. The marsupial cat (or Tasmanian devil) and the marsupial wolf were driven into the most remote Tasmanian forests. Today, in a part of the earth that was once almost devoid of human beings, there are over a hundred million domestic animals as well as eleven million human beings! It is the same in Africa. The lion and the leopard have disappeared from the Atlas region, and in the Sahara the Mendes antelope and the ostrich have become very rare. When the first settlers advanced into the interior of North America they were deeply impressed by the abundance of wild life which they met. Sixty million bison and innumerable herds of deer and antelope

---

Edible snails close their shells with a lid and thus protect themselves against drying up during their winter sleep. (Photo: A. Niestle/Bavaria)—Black slug in movement. (Photo: W. Harstrick/Bavaria.)

The sundew, an insectivorous plant of Northern Europe.

The stinging nettle's poisonous hairs, greatly magnified. (Photos: Harald Doering.)

wandered about. These huge masses of animals have disappeared; relatively few live in the game reserves. In South America it is mainly the cattle ranchers who hunt the native big game. In the Argentine, for example, the large packs of guanacos (wild llamas), which Darwin encountered 130 years ago, have been exterminated. Various interesting varieties of deer are growing rarer and rarer; the maned wolf, a huge fox of the Argentinian pampas, now occurs only in isolated places. Even in the regions covered by virgin forest the animal kingdom is continually losing living space, for the forests are being felled and converted into neat plantations. Finally, in Asia, by the early years of this century the wild camel, the wild horse of the steppes and the Mongolian wild ass had disappeared for ever. Many wild animals can be rescued at the last minute from ignorance and boundless greed by means of protective measures—as in the case of the white rhinoceros in Africa—but this seems to be only a postponement. The fundamental problem is the enormous increase in numbers of both man and his domestic animals, an increase which threatens to wreck the natural equilibrium completely.

EFFECT OF WEATHER

The weather may be of decisive importance in the balance of a living community, in so far as it can affect the density of the population. Cold and damp check the increase of many creatures; warmth and dryness on the other hand usually have favourable effects. In particular, cold winters are harmful to creatures which actually live in the ground and whose main periods of activity lie in early spring or late autumn; good examples are earthworms and insect larvae. Creatures which winter above ground are unfavourably affected by wet winters with widely fluctuating temperatures; in these conditions their numbers drop considerably. Severe storms, hail and whirlwinds destroy large quantities of tiny creatures and often have very harmful effects on numerous small mammals.

NATURAL CONTROLS

In the West Indies the giant toad has proved to be the most effective opponent of cockchafer grubs, which can be a serious danger to the sugar cane plantations. Whenever dry years cause a

---

"Ink-stroke algae" make the rock faces look as if a bottle of ink had been poured down them. (Photo: O. Jaag)—Beaker and reindeer lichens. (Photo: W. Harstrick/Bavaria.)

drop in the number of toads there is immediately a sharp rise in the number of cockchafer grubs. Mice often considerably reduce the density of insects which spend the winter as chrysalises in the rotting vegetation on the surface of the ground. Wild boars can clear the ground of mice, cockchafer grubs, wire-worms, and the caterpillars and chrysalises of butterflies. And of recent years man has been combating the phenomenon of over-population by means of so-called biological control, using fungi against cockchafer grubs, bacteria against Japanese beetle grubs, viruses against rabbits, and so on.

Insect larvae and chrysalises. From left to right: larva of the Pericoma—*butter-fly midge with a double row of chalky incrustations (5 millimetres); chrysalis of* Machimus, *a predatory fly (after Melin, altered); chrysalis of* Myrmeleon, *the ant-lion (after Sundermeler, altered); larva of the hump-backed fly (*Paraspini-phora*), a typical inhabitant of carrion, dung and human corpses (after Keilin, altered).*

Quite often cannibalism breaks out among insects; eggs and chrysalises are the victims. This phenomenon also occurs among fieldmice and some kinds of lizards on isolated islands. It has even been observed among amoebas and ciliate infusoria of the edaphon; the latter can positively hunt each other. Mass emigration, too, of the sort practised by rats and lemmings, can lead in cases of severe over-population to effective self-limitation. All these emigrations end in death and destruction: millions of creatures are carried off by disease or eaten by beasts of prey; innumerable others drown when they try to cross a river or a lake, or else perish from exhaustion. So far as lemmings are concerned, none of those that emigrate ever returns to its original home, and only seldom does emigration lead to the settlement of fresh territory. The emigration more or less peters out, for rodents make very definite demands on their living space and are not easily satisfied. There is now room enough again for a new upsurge of life in the old home for those who have stayed behind, until one day the space becomes too congested for them as well, and the need arises for a fresh emigration and a fresh wave of death.

The rise in the products of metabolism and a shortage of food can also lead to a worsening in conditions and hence to the limitation or even complete collapse of a mass increase in numbers. Lack of food is often mainly responsible for the decimation of excessive numbers of fieldmice and cockchafer grubs. As a rule, living creatures only start to do economic damage when they overstep the bounds of their normal reproductive rate. When numbers are normal, every organism has its job to do in the interplay of forces: small mammals loosen and aerate the soil; termites, so injurious to buildings, do the same when they fill the earth with holes, so that heavy tropical downpours can quickly drain away. In grassland, wire worms (click beetle larvae) and cockchafer grubs, which are so harmful when there are too many of them, help to thin out the grass so that the vegetation can be renewed.

METHODS OF DEFENCE

Plants cannot run away, but even they can defend themselves. Some secrete bitter substances, with which they impart an unpleasant taste to leaves and fruit; others defend themselves with acids and poisons, with nauseating milky fluids, with stinging hairs, prickles, thorns and crystal needles. They have in fact innumerable ways of protecting themselves, at least partially, from their 'enemies'. Even among themselves it is not all friendship. Quite apart from the competition for light, water and food, there is the amazing pheno-menon of a sort of 'chemical warfare' between higher plants. This occurs mainly on poor soil and in unfavourable climatic conditions. For example, wormwood interferes with other plants growing near it and can even cause them to die. This effect extends for about a yard all round and makes itself apparent mainly in the reduced growth of neighbouring plants. It is now known that the cause is a chemical substance which the wormwood produces in the fine hairs on its leaves. Every time it rains this substance is washed off the surface of the leaves and poisons the immediate neighbourhood afresh. It is also known that in the hot deserts of North America there are many bushes under which no other plant can thrive. Their leaves have been analysed and likewise found to contain a substance which inhibits the growth of other plants. The leaves of these bushes have only to fall to the ground to poison it for other plants. Some desert shrubs diffuse in the surrounding soil, through their roots, a chemical substance which keeps away competitors for the little food available.

Animals have many ways of protecting themselves. Some have claws, others kill their opponents by their muscular strength, by biting them, or with the poison in their teeth or their sting; that is, if the swiftness of their legs or wings does not make flight seem more prudent than resistance. It is precisely the contrasts in equipment and instincts, and the great variations in methods of fighting and hiding, hunting and fleeing, adaptation and protection, which enable innumerable different species to survive. Cunning and speed match brute strength, toughness matches shrewdness and keen sight, fertility matches longevity, deadly poison matches insatiable greed, and so on in an endless series of complicated variations.

Thus amid all these hostile phenomena protection against the aggressor is a very important factor. As we have said, organisms are equipped with the most varied means of defending themselves actively or passively: prickles and armour, unpleasant effluvia and corrosive fluids, immobility and intimidating postures, camouflage and imitation. Most means of active defence are similar to those of attack: they are weapons for striking, biting and stinging. These are most familiar in vertebrates, but they also occur in the insect world. Leaf bugs emit from tubes in their back a secretion which gums up the jaws of aggressive parasites; the larvae of certain wasps squirt blood; the larvae of shield beetles direct their mask of dung against their attackers. Bombardier beetles, which are found all over the world, emit from their glands a pungent fluid which explodes into a gas when it comes into contact with the air. These beetles fire a series of four or five shots of this fluid against their attackers. Many slow worms, and also the glass snakes, squirt an evil-smelling liquid out of their anus and try to soil their opponent with it. When they are in danger, horned toads squirt a fine stream of blood out of the lower part of their eyelids. This stream of blood can travel a distance of up to a yard. Every animal keeps out of the way of the African polecat for the stream from its stink gland spreads a terrible smell and is also directed so accurately that many an eye has been blinded by it. The funny little chipmunks and kangaroo mice of the desert defend themselves against the attacks of their arch-enemies, lizards and snakes, by throwing sand over them at tremendous speed. Poison is used to increase the efficiency of the attack by numerous groups of creatures—spiders, wasps, centipedes and snakes. Scorpions try to cripple their assailant with the poisonous sting at the hinder end of their bodies. Vipers, and many North American lizards which have poison glands behind their jaws, are very much feared for their bite. The quantity and appearance of the poison vary from species to species: it can be colourless, as in the case of the cobra; yellow, as in the case of the rattlesnake; or white, as in the case of the copper-head snake. Among snake poisons there are nerve poisons, which affect the breathing, and blood poisons, which destroy the red corpuscles or so damage the blood vessels that they allow bleeding. Curiously enough, many animal poisons—cobra poison, for example —when taken down the alimentary canal—that is, through the mouth—can hardly be described as poisonous at all; being mostly protein in nature, they can be digested in the gut and only act as a poison when they are introduced directly into the blood stream. Moreover, at least a certain degree of immunization can be attained; Indian snake-charmers seem to immunize themselves actively against snake bites.

Certain land animals deal out knocks and blows. A good example is the apparently clumsy giant ant-eater, whose muscular forelegs with their sharp claws are effective close-combat weapons feared even by the predatory cats. The legs of the ostrich, too, are so strong that they form a defensive weapon which commands respect. An ostrich is perfectly capable of breaking an aggressive hyena's back with a well-aimed kick. Giraffes, too, use their powerful hooves to defend themselves and their young, and even the most dangerous beasts of prey can be put out of action by one single blow. Numerous creatures of the ground have developed the principle of uniting forces in order to increase their powers of attack and defences. Some species of tropical ants successfully follow on a small scale the practice of wolves and hunt in packs. The notorious driver ants join together in giant 'army columns', organize plundering expeditions thousands strong and proceed to drive before them the whole animal population of the area which they attack. They explore all the plants, all the clefts and chinks in the ground, even houses, and bite to death every creature which does not take to flight in time—insects, worms, snails, amphibians and mice; anything into which they get their jaws is left a bare skeleton. They are real nomads, travelling from one resting-place to another. Twenty-day rest periods alternate with somewhat shorter periods of wandering. These phases, only disclosed by comparatively recent observations, are determined by the periodic events in the life of the queen (swelling of the ovaries and laying of eggs).

Almost as numerous are the passive means of defence, employed by animals in an attempt to escape being seen or directly attacked by their enemies, through defensive behaviour, by warning devices or by trying to camouflage themselves. At the approach of danger, beetles allow themselves to relax completely and remain absolutely motionless; mites roll into a crack in the earth, where they are certainly difficult to find. Many birds that roost on the ground press themselves firmly against the ground, so that they can only be discovered with real difficulty. The heron stretches its breast, neck and beak bolt upright towards the sky and lets other creatures approach almost to within touching distance. When they sense danger, most creatures do not rush blindly off but first of all stop as if rooted to the spot and wait to see what the suspected enemy does next. Wild cats bend down, martens go as stiff as a poker, rodents straighten up silently. In many creatures which are tied to the ground hiding is the most natural means of protection. The prairie dog or barking squirrel, whose legs cannot carry it fast enough, digs itself into the ground of the savannah. Many insects hide in the earth or in rotting vegetation, where they can also keep their eggs safe, or else they build envelopes round their bodies out of wax, resin, other secretions or even their own excrement. In the case of many ground mites the hairs and bristles on the body are coated with a crust of sticky particles of sand and earth, empty egg shells and the remains of the skins of earlier stages of development; this is an example of 'dirt mimicry', which gives the creatures a close resemblance to their surroundings, thus protecting them from attack. Many ants, wasps, and spiders protect themselves by erecting earthy or web-like barricades at the entrance to their dwellings. The same rôle can also be played by 'phragmosis', in which a specially adapted part of the body serves to block a cave or nest. For example, the soldiers of the North American *Colobopsis* ant have a flattened head so shaped that it fits exactly into the entrance of the nest. Only the correct 'password'—the right, well-known nest smell—will induce the gatekeeper to open the way to the returning workers. Certain cave-dwelling spiders close the entrance not with a lid or web but with their own hindquarters, which drop sharply and fit into the hole like a cork in a bottle. The cave toad possesses a horny head which corresponds exactly to the diameter of its hole in the ground. In edentates of the genus *Chlamyphorus*, which also live in subterranean holes, the hind part of the body is provided with a bony shield which completely blocks the hole. A well-known example of phragmosis is provided by the South American armadillo mole or fairy armadillo, which leads a subterranean life like the common or garden mole. These armadillos, which are hardly six inches long, seldom come up to the surface and even when they do they never stray far from their burrows. When danger threatens they flee head first into their burrows, curl their spoon-shaped tails over their bodies, and close the entrance to the protective subterranean tunnel with their bony hindquarters.

Other ground creatures, especially beetles, protect themselves by a special capacity for running and jumping, or by the ability to hurl themselves off as if from a catapult with the aid of a joint in the neck. This jumping mechanism is well known from click beetles, which are found all over the world. In the big varieties of click beetle it may well serve as a direct defence against enemies—birds, lizards, and so on—in so far as the force applied to use the click mechanism—quite apart from the momentary surprise it causes—will often be sufficient to cause the assailant to loosen its grip. Other devices for self-preservation are smooth outer skeletons which offer no grip; these are characteristic of many carrion beetles, of pill bugs and horned mites. The same method is employed by those powerful diggers the armadillos of the American continent, which can roll up into a perfect ball like a hedgehog and are thus practically unassailable. An example of defence by inflation is provided by an African species of toad, which increases its size so much by this method that many snakes cannot overpower it. Many tortoises can clamp their belly armour firmly to their carapace or back armour by means of a connecting hinge joint; others can drop the hind part of their carapace like a visor.

Many land creatures possess devices for frightening their adversaries. The horned toad, a native of the Asiatic steppes and in itself quite harmless, suddenly changes its appearance when it believes it is threatened. It opens its jaws wide in fury and the folds of skin at the corners of its mouth expand into big discs. The teeth stick out threateningly from the apparently enormous mouth, which is bright red as a result of the rush of blood to it. Another animal which behaves in much the same way is the Australian bearded lizard, which feeds on mice and large insects. If an enemy approaches, it opens its jaws with their powerful teeth in a threatening way and at the same time erects a huge, prickly, bright yellow and scarlet ruff, which sticks out all round the creature's neck like a great shield. The brightly coloured face of the mandrill—it varies from pillar-box red to cobalt blue—certainly frightens away all the inhabitants of the virgin forest, and the natives try to keep out of the way of this huge, spiteful, bad-tempered animal.

The 'danger' factor has given rise to all kinds of warning sounds and cries of alarm in wild creatures; the barking of baboons, which post sentinels and spies everywhere, the low cry with which the red fox warns its cubs, the piping sounds of marmots and squirrels, and the grunting of the wild boar, which causes the whole pack to disappear almost without a sound, are but a few examples. Sometimes the warning behaviour of certain birds can afford protection to other kinds of creatures. A good example of this is provided by the crocodile bird, which feeds on worms and insects in the crevices of the crocodile's hide and with its warning cry can make the creature dive. The same sort of function is fulfilled by the ox-bird, frequently found on cattle and rhinoceroses. Birds that roost in colonies seek to frighten away enemies by making a deafening noise; herds of hooved animals protect themselves by bellowing; the rattlesnake agitates its warning rattle when it feels itself threatened; and the gorilla warns its family by opening its mouth and banging its cheek with its hand.

CAMOUFLAGE

Many creatures seek to camouflage themselves, either by merging with the general background colour of their surroundings or by making the shape of their bodies similar to their surroundings. Protective coloration is particularly important in the open expanses of the desert and the snowy wastes of the polar regions. Among desert animals we find numerous examples of excellent merging with the colour of the ground. Some species of wasps, and also the black beetles already mentioned several times, receive a silvery appearance through light-coloured or white hairs, scales or hoop-like coats of wax. Desert larks show amazing adaptations to the colour of the ground, as surprising observations in the Namib desert confirmed. Red larks there live on red soil, dark-coloured ones on dark soil, and the light-coloured ones only on light soil. What is of particular significance is that where two differently coloured soils meet, each

Over seven feet tall and fifteen feet long, the broad-mouthed rhinoceros, also known as the white rhinoceros, is the largest land mammal after the elephant. (Photo: Zoological Society of London.)

Termite nests are the most impressive example of the movement of earth by insects.
(Photo: Dr A. Lindgens.)

kind of lark sticks strictly to his own appropriately coloured territory. Attempts to drive larks from red sand soil to the adjacent rock covered with light-coloured calcareous plants, or vice versa, were quite unavailing. Further examples of protective coloration in desert creatures are to be found in numerous snakes, lizards, spiders, and insects. In North America two species of pouched mice occur side by side, one on gleaming white gypsum, the other on black lava.

Nature never hesitates to perfect an animal's camouflage with a few deft touches. The tiger's richly coloured skin merges perfectly

Phragmosis in Ants
Soldier of the Colobopsis ants (North America)
closes the entrance to the nest with his exception-
ally big head, which fits the hole like a cork.

with the surroundings, thanks to its stripes and flecks. The zebra's stripes, the leopard's spots, the giraffe's lattice-work pattern are all touches of camouflage which blur the animal's outline against its background most effectively. It is not for nothing that young lions, pumas, and lynxes, whose parents are all a plain yellowish-brown, and also most young deer, have a spotted coat, which is almost invisible amid the tangled vegetation of the jungle. Similar if not quite such extreme alterations of colour are displayed in the desert and on the savannah by many other mammals, reptiles, and insects. The way in which land amphibians camouflage themselves by adapting their coloration to their surroundings is particularly striking. A good example is the common toad; the colour of its skin varies from a dark greyish brown via a dirty olive colour to the deep black of many specimens. Since the body is also covered with wart-like bumps, when the creature is at rest it can hardly be distinguished from the ground. It is the same with the orange-speckled toad, whose back is the colour of muddy earth. Even the bright-coloured amphibians of the tropical rain forest merge amazingly well with their usually bright and variegated if unevenly lit environment. In addition, physiological conditions, the weather, and in particular variations in light can all provoke changes of colour. The creatures concerned all possess in their skins special cells containing particles of colour pigment. These cells can expand and contract, so that the

161

L

light or dark pigments—under the influence of hormones—adopt different distributions, without any alteration in the total quantity of pigment present. In the case of the grasshoppers of Asia Minor a whole range of colours can be observed, whose various shades correspond exactly to nuances in the coloration of the ground. Each particular variety is confined to ground of a similar colour—an area which may amount to only a few square yards. We frequently find quite good adaptations to the colour of the ground in creatures outside desert areas. In these cases the predominant colour is an earthy brown. Good examples are certain birds that roost on the ground and above all small rodents and beasts of prey. In virgin forest, too, all kinds of dark shades are common.

A further refinement in the way of camouflage is the deceptive resemblance of many insects to leaves, pieces of wood, lichens, bark and similar objects. This so-called mimesis is effected in many creatures resembling bark or lichens in colour with the aid of folds of skin. A very well known example is the gecko; it has flaps of skin on the rump, tail, and limbs which blur the outline of its body. The little tequexin lizards of the forests of Panama and Colombia are quite invisible against the background of the forest floor; thanks to their dark colour, their slender bodies—their backs are made to look rough by a few cross rows of enlarged scales—and their slow movement, which gives way to complete immobility as soon as danger threatens, they look like twigs or pieces of wood lying on the ground. A number of insects can look like lichens or the bark of a tree. This similarity is produced by a large number of small warts, projections and jagged edges on the rings at the back of the body. We meet this 'lichen mimesis' in many arthropods, such as spiders and a snout beetle from Madagascar. All these creatures are completely invisible in their normal surroundings.

MIMICRY

Another facet of this kind of behaviour is the imitation of other creatures. There are various bugs, belonging to quite different families, which have a decided resemblance to ants. They are of about the same size, gleaming black in colour, have medium-length legs, a clearly separated head, and the typical waist between the thorax and abdomen. They have stubby wings and move like ants. The biological significance of these resemblances is that the ants, which investigate these lodgers in their nests with their feelers, are deceived by the ant-like shape. Certain beetles, too, and a few small spiders imitate the posture and behaviour of ants. North American spiders carry this imitation to the point of trying to hide the fact that they have eight legs by keeping the first pair well stretched out in front. Harmless butterflies and flies assume the shape and character of hornets, bees, wasps, and bumble-bees, and are thus respectfully

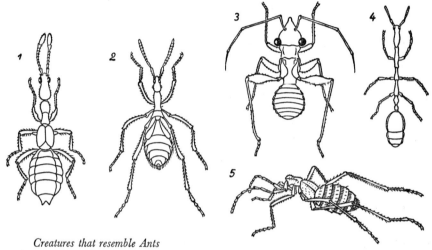

Creatures that resemble Ants

1. Mimeciton, *a beetle.* 2. Ecitomorpha, *beetles that imitate ants in shape and movement.* 3. Myrmecophyes, *an Eastern European bug with a typical resemblance to ants.* 4. *The beetle* Mimanomma, *an example of a highly developed imitation of an ant.* 5. Dorylostethus, *a beetle that lives with the driver ant.*

avoided by their foes. It can certainly not be suggested that Nature lacks ideas when it comes to protecting her creatures and making their lives easier, especially where the smaller and weaker species are concerned.

ASSOCIATION AND SYMBIOSIS

The natural striving of organisms to counter predators, parasites and disease-carriers, as well as the difficulties imposed by changing environments, often creates harsh dissonances in the harmony of nature. However, this should not cause us to forget the many cases where creatures which are quite different in nature co-exist peacefully without affecting each other in the slightest. Among land organisms one-sided partnerships of this sort, which benefit one partner and do no harm, or no harm worth speaking of, to the other, are extraordinarily widespread.

163

Let us take the example of neighbourliness and the sharing of lodgings. Cave owls and ground swallows like to live in the burrows of the pampas hare, sheldrake on sea-coasts sometimes inhabit foxes' burrows, and ptarmigan like to be near herds of reindeer, for they can thus more easily reach the vegetation which the reindeer have scratched up from beneath the snow. Desert lizards have a liking for the underground burrows of rodents, not only as living quarters but also as convenient 'larders', where they can eat up the remains of the rodents' meals. Then there is the cohabitation of the tuatara with various kinds of stormy petrels; the birds inhabit the islands of New Zealand in vast numbers and nest in underground holes, which they share with the lizards. In tropical lands birds of the most varied species frequent the neighbourhood of bees' and wasps' nests. In Africa some species of ants admit the lichen woodpecker (it resembles the European green woodpecker) quite unmolested into their nests, although the latter repays the hospitality in the most shameful way by devouring the larvae and chrysalises of its hosts. Several species of kingfisher and parrot regularly lay their eggs in the extensive nests of termites, in which they make holes—just as their relatives bore holes in tree trunks. Net worms, which are found as far north as Spain and are deceptively like earthworms, usually inhabit the nests of ants and termites, on whose larvae they feed. It is still an unsolved mystery why driver ants and termites, which are not afraid of tackling even a snake, allow these blind worms to live in their communities.

There are innumerable cases of creatures lodging in the nests of warm-blooded animals and insects, where they find moist air, uniform warmth, darkness and protection, apart from the welcome remains of the nest-owner's food and droppings. Beetles, mites, and the larvae of flies and fleas live in the holes of sand martins, rodents, and moles; simple insects, lice, and small beetles live in the nests of bumble bees and wasps. But the number and variety of these lodging arrangements first become really clear when we consider the variety of guests entertained by ants and termites. Unlike genuine guests, lodgers are not protected and cared for; they are only tolerated. Certain rove beetles, which occur among the various species of forest ants, have a striking similarity in colour to their hosts. Among red ants one finds only brown beetles, and most of the guests of the brown ants are brown too. If, in spite of the similarity, the ants become suspicious, the beetles rely on their shape; they do not run off, but press their unusually flat bodies close against the ground, so that the ants find it almost impossible to get a grip on them. The short beetles too, which are widely found playing the part of unnoticed lodgers, are more or less safe from attack thanks to their smooth armour. It is the same with springtails and silverfish, which cannot be attacked by their ant hosts because of their small size and great speed. Certain ground beetles which live in ants' nests can be mistaken for pieces of

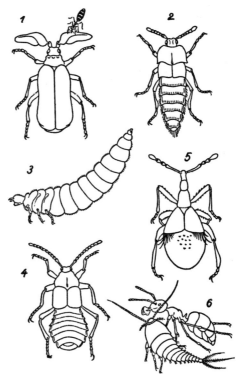

Examples of Tolerated Neighbour-liness

1. *Antenna beetle* (Paussus) *with ant.*
2. *Dinarda* beetle, *a guest tolerated by ants.*
3/4. *Lomechusa* beetle larva *and imago, true nest parasite among predatory ants.*
5. *Claviger,* club beetle, gladly *tolerated in ants' nests because of its excretions.*
6. *Silverfish as a guest of ants.*

wood; others could be taken for seeds, and sack-beetle larvae, which are wrapped in dung, look deceptively like little lumps of sand. Small mites, simple insects, tiny wingless crickets, and small cockroaches climb round the ants' heads and legs, always on the lookout to snatch some of the ants' food. It is only their small size and their nimbleness which ensure that they remain undisturbed in their activities.

The 'gilled fauna' of the European land isopods provide an example of lodging that may at first seem extreme. As is well known, these creatures take the moisture needed for breathing through gills from their surroundings in the form of rainwater, dew and the absorption water in the ground, holding it fast partly between and partly under the gill covers. These tiny 'micro-aquariums' provide miniature habitats for certain ciliates and wheel animals, which for their part show marked adaptations to their curious living space.

Many plants, too, have organisms as lodgers, though it is true that they do not derive any benefits from them. For example, numerous ants and other insects live in the leaf-sheath bulges of the pineapple plants of the American tropical and sub-tropical regions, and also in the hollow thorns of the Mexican acacia. This may seem at first pure chance. But when we note that the feathery leaves of the acacia have oily and albuminous corpuscles at their ends, and when we further observe that when an acacia is touched the ants living in the thorns stream out and rush on the creatures which came too near the plant, we cannot avoid speaking of a symbiosis, a relationship bringing mutual advantages. The plant provides food and lodging, the creature—here the ant—protects the plant against other interlopers. The symbiotic character of this association is confirmed by the following observation: young acacias grown in a garden and not colonized by ants are often stripped of all their foliage by leaf-cutter ants; on the other hand, wild acacias, which have 'their own' ants as tenants, are always spared by the leaf-cutter ant. The water cells in the leaves of European turf mosses regularly have lodgers, to wit certain flagellates and wheel animals.

In this connection a noteworthy association is the quite unparasitic one between certain small creatures and the widely distributed insectivorous pitcher plants of the tropical forests. The species which

Insectivorous pitcher plant of the virgin forest. Nepenthes ampullaria, *piece of root with 'pitchers'.*

particularly interest us here are the earth-bound ones, whose pitchers, hidden in thick foliage and humus, are filled with captured isopods, spiders, beetles, millipedes, and even, quite often, snails. In the midst of this mash of partly killed or already decomposing creatures lives a host of tiny organisms which have taken up permanent quarters there, without themselves being harmed or killed by the digestive glands. The most prominent of these inhabitants of pitcher plants are the larvae of flies and midges, mites and threadworms, some of them with a very curious appearance.

Another phenomenon that is widespread among land animals is temporary association for the purpose of transport. If mites regularly appear quite early and in large numbers on corpses, it is largely because they cling to the bodies of carrion and dung beetles and thus have themselves been carried from one source of food to another. Hair worms reach their food supply easily and quickly on gnats and louse flies; gooseberry mites make use of aphids for this purpose, oil-beetle larvae travel on bees, and threadworms on carrion-frequenting beetles, mites and earthworms. Many dung-eating beetles let themselves be carried around in the coats of mammals, sitting near the anus while the animal is in movement.

PARASITES—EXTERNAL AND INTERNAL

In many ways it is only a small step from a predatory mode of life and one-sided exploitation to a parasitic mode of life. Unicellular internal parasites are legion. Land creatures of every sort—even the unicellular edaphic organisms themselves—are attacked and every possible site in the host's body is utilized. A favourite spot in the higher animals is the intestinal canal; protozoa are easily carried into it in the form of cysts or spores with the food. It is true that the vast majority of them soon perish; the easiest locality for them to settle is the large intestine, where the processes of digestion are more or less finished. There is little to prevent these temporary sojourners in the intestine from becoming true intestinal parasites. There must be a highly developed ability to resist the effect of digestive fermentations. The blood cells and the internal cells of the blood vessels, indeed in vertebrates the whole inside of the body, are also favoured by parasitic protozoa. Parasites may either move freely or else cling on with special devices to the cell walls (spore animalcules in earthworms; flagellates in rodents). Others of these uninvited guests lie between the cells like certain spore animalcules, which live exclusively in the muscle tissue of field mice, hamsters, and rabbits (tissue parasitism). Others again spare no organ and no kind of tissue, and penetrate right into the cell protoplasm (for example, cell parasites in millipedes) or attack the nucleus of the cell (nucleic parasitism—common in the intestine of the mole).

Blood parasitism is as widespread as intestinal parasitism. There is no doubt that in many cases it is derived from intestinal parasitism, for it can be observed, especially in reptiles and small mammals, that true intestinal flagellates occasionally pass into the blood, and that they not only stay there quite a long time but even multiply. When the infection of a vertebrate continues to start in the intestine even where a carrier—a louse or a flea—is interposed, it becomes

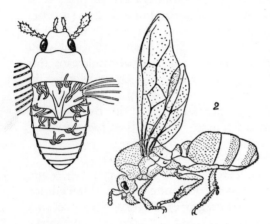

Examples of Association for Transport (Phoresy)

1. Beetle attacked by threadworm larvae. The larvae perch between the rings of the back.

2. The Carebara *ant (queen) takes two little female workers from the nest with it on its wedding flight. (After Wheeler, altered.)*

quite clear that the intestine is the original source. For example, a rat can infect itself with a blood parasite by licking from its skin the infected excrement deposited there during their blood-sucking activities by the fleas or lice which carry the parasite.

Nature has many ways of preserving and spreading unicellular parasites. 'Change of host' is very frequent; what happens in most cases is that part of the parasite's development takes place in a species of creature which is eaten by the original host. Thus an intestinal parasite in the form of a cyst can easily be absorbed by a herbivore with its food; in the case of a carnivore this only works as a rule if among its prey there are creatures which happen to harbour the cysts in their intestines. For example, the mole infects itself by devouring earthworms which for their part have eaten mole excrement containing cysts. This change of host can link the most widely differing organisms. To take a few further examples, the liver fluke forms a link between snails and ruminants; the tapeworm from the rabbit's intestine lives in grass mites in the form of bladder worm; the *Coccidia*, which are spore animalcules, occur in millipedes and earthworms, which are eaten by the mole; the flagellate *Leptomonas* from the large intestine of the gecko lives in desert bugs; the *Leish-mania* flagellates, which cause kala-azar ('black fever'), occur in the intestine of certain sandflies and also in rats, mice and hamsters; and the many species of *Trypanosoma* are found in the intestines of tsetse flies, mouse fleas, hamsters, dormice, moles, badgers and ant-eaters. Many domestic animals, and also rodents, apes and birds, can be carriers of the tiny two-micron-long *Toxoplasma* agent and thus become the seat of infection for human toxoplasmosis. This becomes particularly dangerous when the agent passes into the embryo in the mother's body; the result can be still-births and unnatural births, eye trouble, fits and idiocy.

The widely distributed species of the *Phytmonas* genus of flagellates alternate between insects and plants. These unicellular organisms are found in the milky juice of the spurge; they also occur in some nettles, especially tropical and subtropical species. The carrier insects are bugs which suck plant saps. The flagellates absorbed into the intestine together with the sap increase rapidly in the first few days. From the eighth onward they

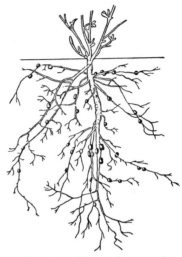

Bacteria nodules on the roots of leguminous plants.

move into the saliva glands, whence they are returned to the plant when the bug feeds again.

Besides the sort of parasitism which consists of a conflict between host and parasite and may involve fairly serious damage to both parties, there are also dependent relationships in which each partner receives vital assistance from the other. In nutritional associations of this sort, which are called symbioses, the two organisms concerned have become interdependent and could no longer exist apart. This form of 'mutual service' is widespread.

So far we have indubitably recognized only a small proportion of these symbioses. In the vegetable kingdom, the alliance between algae and fungi which occurs in lichens, the mycorrhiza between fungi and seed plants, and the bacteria-filled nodules on the roots of leguminous plants, are all regarded as examples of symbiosis.

169

Among the lichens that inhabit earth and humus there are 'choosy' species which only thrive on particular soils. In the Alps, for instance, the most striking difference between the individual communities is a strict division between lime and gravel lichens. The former prefer a basic rock foundation, the latter are adapted to mountain soil derived from acid rock. The most important acid-loving group is the community of map lichens. Their crusts cling close to the rock and display numerous black lines; they come from the dark deposit of the lichen fungus.

Finally, other very interesting lichens are the 'ornithocoprophilous' nitrogen lichens, which specialize in the utilization of nitrogen and settle for preference on over-manured birds' nesting and resting places on rocks. They are also found on marmots' burrows. Members of this group are the orange-red crustaceous lichen, which is found at high altitudes in the Alps, and the rust-red placentiform-lichen, which is common on birds' roosting places in the mountains. It is interesting to reflect what a difference there is in nitrogen requirements between a nitrogen-loving lichen and a wart lichen embedded in the bare limestone rock; the latter has to rely on the nitrogen in the rainwater—a quantity so small that it cannot be measured chemically.

For a long time lichenology was a somewhat neglected branch of botany. The situation changed when some fifteen years ago Japanese, Finnish, and Swedish biochemists established that many of the characteristic metabolic products of lichens had an antibiotic effect, and when American microbiologists found that other lichen substances showed organic links which could activate metal atoms and thus, among other things, increase the effect of mineral fertilizers.

Another widespread phenomenon is the mycorrhizal state; that is, the association of a fungus with a higher plant. The roots of most European forest trees, and of birches, willows, heather, enzian, lilies, and many grasses, live in association with webs of fungi, which either completely invest the roots with a mantle of threads or else penetrate the cortex cells of the roots by dissolving the epidermis or by travelling up the hairs on the roots. The mycorrhizal state is formed by alga-like fungi, by pipe fungi and by stalked fungi, including tube forms and hybrids. Most of these fungi do not seem to specialize in any one particular host; that is, the same plant can be associated with various fungi, and the same species of fungus can settle on different hosts. Thus the well-known fly agaric forms a mycorrhiza with firs, pines, larches, and birches. In most cases this alliance is indubitably a true symbiosis. The partners benefit each other by providing one another with certain foodstuffs. The fungus must be regarded first and foremost as a supplier of nitrogen to the higher plant; without the intermediary assistance of a fungus the higher plant can draw only inorganic nitrogen out of the soil. The host takes over this fungus protein by dissolving the walls of the fungus threads in its root cells and 'digesting' the protoplasm thus released. The fungus for its part draws in general from the higher plant the carbohydrates which the plant can constantly provide through its assimilation of carbonic acid. Although many plants thrive through mycorrhiza, it is known that they do not have to rely on it; this is true, for example, of many heathers. On the other hand, there are also cases where the mycorrhiza has become an absolutely vital necessity. Good examples of this are provided by orchids, whose usually small seeds, which are poor in reserve substances (oil, protein), can hardly germinate or develop without the presence of mycorrhizal fungi. In the case of these orchids—the bird's nest orchid, for example—which possess hardly any chlorophyll of their own, it is quite understandable that the higher plant must draw all the foodstuffs it needs, including carbohydrates, from the fungus on which it is a regular parasite.

Of all the many symbioses to be found in life on land, those of the animal kingdom display some of the most interesting and informative characteristics; not least because the maintenance of these associations during the lives of the two partners and afterwards in succeeding generations demands special adaptations. These adaptations are not the work of a day; they have taken innumerable generations to reach what is often a functional perfection. The degeneration of a symbiosis, when one of the partners breaks up the association and destroys the other, can also be extremely interesting, because it throws light on the origin of symbiosis in general.

A good example of a purely nutritional symbiosis is the cultivation of fungi by the termites and leaf-cutting ants of South America. These creatures are not satisfied with collecting their food; they also cultivate the kind which suits them, namely fungi, in their nests. This phenomenon is thus best compared with the human activity of mushroom-growing rather than with tilling the soil, as it was once. The ants do in fact go about their task just like our mushroom-growers: they lay beds of manure. The necessary material is cut from every conceivable plant and carried into the nest in long processions. In the nest the pieces of leaf are chewed up and this vegetable pulp goes to make the dung beds or fungus gardens, which are then planted with fungi by the ants. The plants thrive in their beds and are continually bitten off by the ants so that they do not shoot up too high. Tube- or club-shaped thickenings are formed, which are eminently suitable for food, especially for the young ants, since they contain, as we now know, important substances. In the case of the Brazilian atta ants we also know precisely how the fungus is transplanted from one colony to another and handed on as a 'legacy' from one generation to another. When the queen prepares for the wedding flight she always takes little pieces of fungus from the maternal home with her, in a sort of pouch underneath the mouth. In the fresh foundation her first thought is always for the fungus, which she spits out and manures with her own excrement, so that this vital component is ready to hand when a start is made with the building of the new nest.

Like the ants, termites, too, grow fungi in their nests, in this instance on bits of wood and other sections of plants which they have carried in and worked upon. These fungus gardens differ in shape and size; some are the size of a hazel nut, others as big as a football. They may be roundish, flattened, egg- or pear-shaped, loaf-shaped, or of some other shape. In consistency they are like a sponge, loose and full of holes; the colour varies from light to dark brown. The beds themselves consist of small, tightly compressed balls; unlike those of the ants, they are produced by mastication, but have always been through the bowel and in consequence are mixed with excrement. Like those of ants, the fungus gardens of termites are covered on top with a delicate web, on whose function views differ considerably. What is certain is that the king and queen are fed exclusively on fungus heads; in the intestines of these creatures one never finds particles of wood, but the remains of fungi. The larvae, too, eat nothing but fungi, while it is despised by the workers and soldiers, which prefer particles of wood and other parts of plants, and also often eat their own dead.

Ants have another symbiotic association with other creatures—leaf bugs, shield bugs, and cicadas—which is quite unique. These creatures are kept by ants just as useful animals are kept by man. The lice and cicadas provide sweet, sugary secretions of which the ants are very fond. These creatures are not nesting companions, but the ants look after them carefully and regard them, one might almost say, as 'domestic animals', which they guard, care for and protect, causing them frequently to release their secretions by stroking them. Many ants even erect special buildings for their 'milch lice'. Shield lice and cicadas, as well as leaf lice, yield large quantities of sugary dung, which is licked up by the ants after it has been excreted, or—where the link between the partners is close—coaxed out of the lice by the ants with stroking movements. Indeed, some species of leaf lice can no longer excrete the dung and have to rely completely on their hosts, which then give them regular attention. They carefully roof the lice over with foreign matter, keep their winter eggs in the deeper parts of the nest, carry the larvae out to plants to feed when they

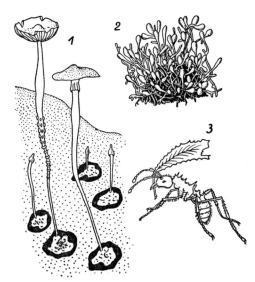

Fungus Cultivation by Termites and Ants

1. *Leaf fungi growing up from the abandoned fungus garden of a termite nest (after Heim, modified).*

2. *Fungus cultivation by leaf- cutter ants.*

3. *Leaf-cutting ant with a piece of leaf.*

hatch, and carry them back into the nest on cold nights. Similar relationships exist between shield lice and certain tropical beetles, and between termites and termite bugs.

The links which we have described as existing between ants and leaf bugs also exist between ants and the caterpillars of the Large Blue Butterfly, which lends a charming animation to summery meadows. The caterpillars, which in shape are reminiscent of cellar isopods, have a number of glands, whose secretions are sought after and licked up by ants. The ants climb on to the caterpillars and work on them with their legs and feelers, whereupon the cater-pillars emit the desired liquid.

In ground creatures with a uniform diet internal symbioses frequently occur, especially in ants and termites again, but also in beetles and bugs that eat decayed matter and even in unicellular creatures. These many protozoa live in very close association with unicellular plants; they are able to benefit from the plants' metabolism as well as from the food which they procure for themselves. Numerous rhizopods and infusoria, especially in peaty turf, which is poor in food and oxygen, display round, green particles in their cytoplasm. These little balls are called zoochlorelles and are lower

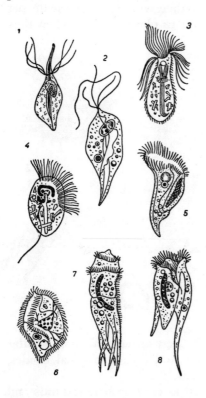

Unicellular Organisms from the Internal Organs of Higher Animals

Symbiotic organisms from the intestines of termites:

1. Oxymonas, *with a long retractable snout and six flagella.*
2. Gigantomonas, *with four flagella and undulating membrane.*
3. Joenia, *with a bundle of body-fixing axial rods.*
4. Parajoenia, *with very fine flagella and a trailing flagellum.*

Symbiotic organisms from insects and mammals:

5. Cunhaia, *from the appendix of the guinea pig.*
6. Nyctotherus, *an internal parasite occurring in beetles.*
7. Ophryoscolex, *a parasite of the hide.*
8. Entodinium, *from the stomach of the sheep.*

plants. However, most of these symbiotic single-celled creatures are also found free from zoochlorelles, and can thrive perfectly well without them. As for the benefits conferred by these symbiotic creatures on their hosts, all that is certain is that the hosts receive oxygen, emitted as a result of photosynthesis. Probably a surplus of vegetable body-building substances, especially carbohydrates, is also delivered, for in some cases it has been shown that creatures containing symbiotic organisms can do without solid food and even without dissolved organic compounds.

Wood-eating beetle larvae carry on the wall of the intestine certain fungi which are likewise utilized for nourishment. Even when it is only a larva, the olive fly fills its middle intestine with certain bacteria from the branches of the olive tree; they help in the process of digestion. Various bugs and lice carry on regular cultures of bacteria in their fatty tissue. In the case of the worker termites, which, unlike the larvae and sexed termites, do not live on the 'harvest' of the fungus gardens but on wood, an amazing variety of flagellates in the intestine help to break down the cellulose. For termites themselves can convert less than a third of the cellulose they eat; the breakdown of the rest is accomplished by symbiotic flagellates, which can amount to a third of the termite's weight. Termites which were experimentally freed from symbiotic organisms by heating (to 99 degrees Fahrenheit or more) soon perished, for they were no longer capable of digesting wood in their usual way. A similar rôle may well be played by the infusoria which live in the digestive organs of mammals with a diet particularly rich in cellulose. In rodents these infusoria inhabit the caecum, in ruminants the stomach and reticulum, in gorillas and chimpanzees the caecum and large intestine. Of course, they are not nearly so important as the termite parasites, for their hosts have incomparably more effective assistance at their disposal, namely cellulose-splitting bacteria. All the same, it is clear that when protozoa are present in large quantities in the food pulp they are not without effect on the total metabolism of the host. It has been established that about eight per cent of infusoria are digested every day, which is a by no means contemptible addition of animal protein and one that is easily utilized.

TERRITORY AND DWELLING PLACES

Most animals do not just wander about; they have a fairly narrowly bounded home territory, a limited individual area, which many never leave throughout their life and which they are ever ready to defend in the breeding season. Of course, the phrase 'home territory' can have a number of very different meanings: for some creatures it means many square miles, for others only a few square yards or inches. Dam and castle, bank and pond are the home of the beaver; here it works away all day, here it rests, and here the little ones are born. The fox, too, has his own territory, where he seeks refuge day in and day out. European songbirds stake out the boundaries of their territory with their various songs, and owls do the same with their characteristic calls.

When the animals of the savannah can see each other, smell and aural communication become less important; if sight is poor and the sense of smell not very well developed, the individual inhabitants of the area make contact with each other through sounds. The howling of jackals, coyotes and wolves, the threatening grunts of the hippopotamus, the loud screaming of the arctic fox and the roar of the lion are unmistakable indications of the connection between territorial possession and the instinctive effort to preserve this personal realm.

The strong local tie naturally creates in wild animals an inner watchfulness and a readiness to defend their rights. Apes will allow no others into their domain. Creatures which gather supplies— marmots, for example—defend their supply dumps.

Many animals build themselves nests, not only as 'cradles' for their young, but also to rest in, like the squirrel, or just to sleep in, like the chimpanzee. The wolf, too, likes to have a good rest in his cave. If you want to accustom a new dog to your company quickly and surely, all you have to do is to let it sleep in your bed with you for a few nights. In this 'cave' the animal quickly overcomes its feeling of strangeness; henceforth the man's house becomes 'its territory', which it is always ready to defend.

Possibly the most strongly marked sense of possession is to be found in the beautifully coloured butterfly lizards of South-east Asia. As far as we know, they are the only reptiles that live the whole year in the same pairs; that is, they are the only monogamous reptiles and consequently the only ones with a true loyalty to one particular place, namely the cave in which they dwell.

Home is simply a question of environment. Many land creatures display a remarkable capacity for returning to their homes. As is well known, in birds the predominant factor is optical orientation in flight; in the case of twilight and nocturnal creatures 'echo-sounding'

Unicellular Organisms. In the circle: Trypanosomes in the blood of toads. Four slender cells and one broad, flattened form of Trypanosoma rotatorium *between the blood corpuscles. Left-hand column, from top to bottom:* Euastrum oblongum *(decorative alga);* Phacus sp. *(flagellate);* Botrydium granulatum *(green alga), an alga attached to soil by branched rhizoids. The whole plant corresponds to a single multinucleate cell.* Arcella *(rhizopod). Centre left:* Euglena deses *(flagellate), with embedded chlorophyll discs and reserve substance. Centre right:* Tabellaria fenestrata, *the zig-zag chain formation of this diatom is an example of shell- and corner-contact through gelatinous excretions. Top right:* Dileptus anser *(infusorian); inside the cell, symbiotic* Zoochlorella *algae. Bottom right:* Protochrysis sp. *(flagellate).*

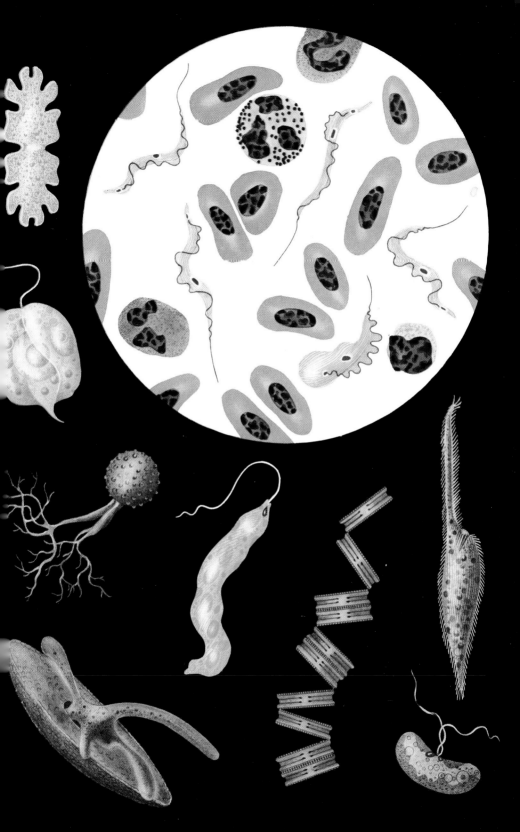

also plays an important part. The flying foxes of India, which sleep in huge companies, return punctually at sunset to their feeding places, which may be as far as twenty miles away. While they are in flight they produce with their tongues curious metallic sounds which give them vital assistance in finding their way.

A good example is that of the mole, which finds its way about its labyrinthine system of underground tunnels with unfailing certainty. These tunnels are all familiar roads to the mole, which can run up and down them either forwards or backwards with equal speed and

*North American sand-dune cricket
in its hole.*

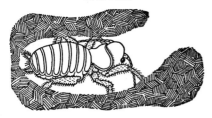

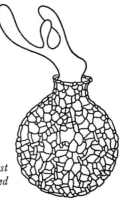

*Difflugia, a rhizopod of the forest
floor with pieces of gravel attached
to its shell.*

skill. It must be assumed that the mole is capable of retracing a path it has already taken before by repeating the same steps again. No doubt the sense of touch plays an important auxiliary rôle, as it does with all blind creatures. If the system of tunnels, or part of it, is destroyed, the mole is able to reconstruct a new system resembling the old one.

Before pupation most insects exude from their skin a hard layer of chitin which protects the chrysalis or pupa. Larvae which do not do this spin a cocoon instead. The material for the envelope is provided by the creature's own body, but the actual work has to be done by the creature itself. We can see from this example how closely instincts are linked to organization. Physiological events, such as the

---

Cave Crustacea. Above: Stygodytes, a blind, unpigmented cave 'shrimp' from the Balkans. Real size about 50 millimetres. Below: Bathynella, one millimetre long, is the smallest known representative of the higher crustaceans. This cave creature, found in Switzerland, Southern France and Roumania, is completely blind.

M

excretion of spinning material, and instinctive actions dovetail with one another; they cannot be separated, for they form a whole.

A special case of instinct is provided by birds, whose nests, with few exceptions, are simply nurseries, or in some cases just cradles for the eggs. As soon as the young birds can fly the nest has fulfilled its purpose, for the nest-building instinct has a temporal connection with the urge to breed and continue the species. Thus only in a few rare cases does the nest form a home for the bird; it needs a protected space only for a brief period. At the end of the breeding season most birds' nests are in such a condition that further occupation is in any case impossible. For whatever pains the parent birds may take to keep the nest clean they cannot prevent the hollow from soon becoming a real breeding-place for mites, ticks and similar parasites. So far as instinctive attachment to one particular place is concerned, we find among the birds that particularly interest us here—that is, those that nest on the ground or in holes—burrowers and masons, simple twig-arrangers, and skilful weavers and moss-workers. The simplest construction to hide the eggs is the quickly scraped hollow in the ground: earth, sand and pebbles are pushed to one side, and the resulting space deepened a little and swept clean. This very modest kind of nest suffices for many birds, especially for chickens, whose young ones leave the nest soon after they have hatched out. Other well-known birds that nest on the ground are ostriches and emus; the males make the hollow. The kiwi, that nearly extinct oddity from New Zealand, lays its exceptionally large and heavy egg under the roots of a tree or else in a very hastily scraped hollow in the ground. Penguins, too, frequently lay their eggs on the bare ground, but mark the nest with a few stones arranged 'symbolically' in a circle. They attach so much importance to these stones which mark their breeding-spaces that they often quarrel violently about them. The black-and-white crocodile bird constructs natural incubators of sand; it buries its eggs deep in the sand of river banks and lets the sun hatch them out. In the same way, the *Megapodius* or big-footed fowl, a distant relative of the pheasant, makes a big mound of grass, leaves and twigs; in due course rain collects in this and turns the whole thing into a seething hot compost heap. The parent birds keep a constant watch on the temperature in this improvised incubator and 'attend' carefully to the ventilation. Each individual egg is constantly checked and each chick is helped to break out of the egg at the right moment by the parents. Once the incubators have been built they are normally used for several years in succession, increasing in extent each year through the care and attention of the parent birds. The hillocks are often twelve to fifteen feet high, with a circumference of twenty yards or more, so that these ground-level nests are the biggest birds' nests in the world. Sand martins, too, are skilful soil engineers; they make deep holes in steep banks of sand or clay. Bee-eaters—brightly coloured tropical birds—make their holes still deeper. Their long, hard, powerful, curved beak makes a decidedly better digging tool than the sand martin's beak. A no less capable miner and tunneller is the gloriously coloured kingfisher. It digs a hole a yard deep in banks of clay or loess, a task for which its bayonet-like beak forms a most effective tool. The building achievements of birds are almost infinite; they range, as we have said, from the humble little cradle for eggs to the huge, unassailable nests of clans and communities.

As for insects, we have only to think of sand bees or earth bees, which dig long passages in sandy soil, leading to several underground breeding chambers. The furry bee digs horizontal tunnels in steep walls of clay. The furrow bee digs quite complicated nests in the earth; different females may work together and so arrange the nests that they have a common exit. A curious additional detail is that a watchman always sits in the exit hole and only lets in those females which live in this common 'apartment'. Some furrow bees behave almost like parasites, leaving eggs in the more or less finished nests of other bees which live in the ground, such as sand bees or silk bees. The mason bee builds real works of art in the form of nests made of grains of sand and mortar which become as hard as iron and can be used by succeeding generations. The nest is finally covered over with further particles of earth. In his way five or six cells are erected next to each other during the cou se of several days. Eventually all the unevennesses are smoothed over by plastering on tiny stones, so that in the end the whole nest looks like a dome-shaped lump of mortar. Different again is the behaviour of the solitary leaf-cutter bee, well known to rose-growers through its irritating habit of cutting semi-circular pieces out of the leaves of their roses. With these little pieces of rose leaf the bee carpets its nest, a habit which is not without deeper significance. The rose leaves contain a good deal of tannic acid, and this prevents the growth of fungus, which would otherwise flourish in the damp tunnel of earth and ruin the pollen and nectar brought home by the bee. Corn-poppy wall bees suck out empty snail shells and install their breeding cells inside them. They also frequently hide the snail-shell under a heap of laboriously collected pine needles and seal it up with sticky saliva. Furry bees make their cells in advance out of clay and sand. First of all they make a main passage in a steep wall of clay. This passage divides into several branches, each of which contains three or four breeding chambers. As soon as all the cells are equipped with food and filled with an egg, the entrance is closed up with a stopper of clay. The striking thing

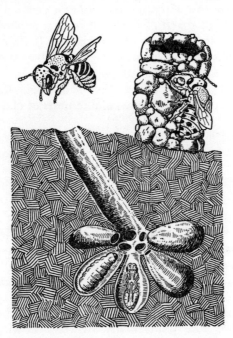

A sand bee flying to its nest (Andrena). Two cells are open. On the surface of the ground can be seen a walled, still open breeding cell of the mortar bee (Chalicodoma). A parasitic bee (Dioxys) waits on it for a chance to lay its eggs.

about these nests is the porch outsid the hole; this porch bends downward like a tap.

There are species of wasps as well as of bees which live a solitary existence, building underground nests for living and breeding. For example there is the universally familiar wall wasp, which betrays its nest in a steep slope of earth by building a downward-curving tube of loose earth outside the hole. There are real architects among the species of wasps which make their nests in hard clay soil. The nests can usually be recognized quite easily by a sort of little chimney which sticks about an inch above the surface of the ground. This chimney is built up out of little particles of clay, a task which the creatures accomplish in a surprisingly short period of time; in half an hour the chimney can rise nearly half an inch. Steep walls of clay provide nesting places for related species of wasps and also for certain solitary bees, which build in a very similar way, but with passages curving downwards. The significance of these chimneys has not been established with any certainty; some authorities think that they may provide protection from parasites.

Another kind of wasp that lives on its own is the well known digging wasp, which hunts all kinds of insects and takes them home as food for its young. These wasps, of which there are many species, dig holes in sandy slopes and similar places with their hind legs. These holes lead, usually through a long passage, to the breeding holes. The wasps drag in food (mainly insects) for the larvae before they

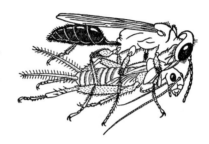

A species of sand wasp which specializes in crickets dragging home its prey, crippled by a sting inserted with anatomical precision.

close the holes up and lay their eggs. Many of them fasten the egg to a thread hanging down from the roof of the hole. It thus floats over the insects and is in no danger of falling among them and being crushed.

TERRITORY

The question of animals' loyalty to a particular spot leads to the further question of everyday life, the question of how a wild creature spends its day. We are so used to the ways of our domestic animals and we know them so well that we lose sight of the behaviour of the wild creature. We know little of its 'way of life' or of 'its world', in which it awakes and moves about day in and day out, builds its dwelling, goes out in search of food, fights its battles with its competitors, breeds, and finally dies. Consequently we tend to entertain a completely false notion of 'wild life'. A wild creature does not wander about aimlessly the livelong day in search of food or of a partner. Certain activities are related to certain times and certain spots in a living space which is, as we now know, clearly defined. This strict enclosure in a system is often important for the life expectancy of individual species. Many wild creatures not only live in a narrowly bounded individual living space but are also largely tied within this territory to certain paths (runs) which lead to water holes, ponds, prey and so on, and are as a rule visited regularly. The hippopotamus makes runs, which are strictly used not only by individual animals but also by whole generations; they are straight corridors, about two feet six inches wide, which stand out clearly from the surrounding country and on sloping ground help the rain water to run away. At many spots these corridors are as much as five feet deep, with walls polished completely smooth by repeated contact with the animals' hides. Sometimes these paths are quite short, perhaps 20 or 30 yards, but often they lead for miles to the grazing grounds in the interior.

Many creatures take action to improve the paths they use regularly; the first step here is to clear away the vegetation that covers the ground. Fieldmouse runs are scrupulously clean; so are the 'witches' paths' which are usually the work of hamsters or hares. Some ants are great road-builders; they clear their runs of all obstacles, and sometimes also make cuttings or roofs over the run with particles of earth, so that a tunnel is produced. When an animal is threatened or disturbed it will sometimes leave its run for the time being and return when all is quiet again.

MATING

Every living creature has an invincible urge to preserve and perpetuate life. However powerful a motive hunger may be in an animal's daily life, sexuality is always a thousand times stronger.

The number of periods of sexual excitement in a year varies from one species to another. Birds usually develop their reproductive glands only in the spring; as for mammals, the pig has only two cycles, while the mare has eight, the rat nine and anthropoid apes twelve or more.

The love play of animals is full of variations. Mammals press themselves together in their sexual excitement, snuggle up to each other and touch each other's bodies with nose, mouth and paws. They can nibble, bite, scratch and stroke, or tug at each other's coats and pull out hairs. Such activities can last minutes, hours or even days before any attempt at copulation is made. The male bird pours out his excitement in song; tropical toads utter trill-like cries and tortoises make fervent hissing and piping noises. Rhinoceroses and tapirs emit whistling sounds; wolves, martens and polecats make grumbling noises, and jackals give vent to long howls. The cock ostrich dances round the hen with comic gravity; the male and female antelope run after each other in a sort of teasing game. Strong males fight one another for desirable females and these disputes often end in the death of one of the contestants. Camel stallions bite and spit; the steppe antelope's antlers become a murderous weapon; baboons stretch up to their full height, open their mouths wide in fury and poke their tongues out; and in their jealousy even lazy sloths fight slow-motion duels with one another.

SLEEP

Many animals' everyday life may be divided into periods of rest and periods of activity. In higher animals it is possible to distinguish activity with spatial movement (walking, crawling, etc.); activity without spatial movement (gnawing, eating, washing, etc.); rest in the sense of physical rest with complete wakefulness; dozing, a kind of semi-sleep frequent, for example, in ruminants; and finally sleep proper. When an animal sleeps it closes the portal to environmental stimuli by reducing its receptivity, and is thus protected from disturbing lights and sounds. Some animals with big ears and particularly sensitive hearing—many pouched rats, for example—fold their ears when they are asleep. Eyes can be protected against undesired light by lids or folds of skin. Instinct ensures that noises indicating danger wake the sleeper, while unimportant ones do not disturb it. Sleeping habits and places differ widely; so does the posture. Most animals sleep on their belly, back or side, but standing and hanging positions also occur. The giraffe sleeps lying down, with its neck either held straight out or bent back in such a way that the head rests on the body. These creatures of the savannah never sleep deeply for more than a quarter of an hour at the most. When the African ostrich is sleeping lightly its body is on the ground, the wings are spread out, and the neck, held straight up (with the eyes closed), performs slow, wobbly, circular movements. In deep sleep, which lasts at the most ten minutes per night, the neck is laid out flat on the ground. No noise or light, however strong, can wake the ostrich during this short period of deep sleep. Elephants usually sleep lying down, and with them, too, the duration of sleep is amazingly short; two to three hours a night at the most. Even this short sleep is not undisturbed, for an elephant has to rise at least once an hour in order to relieve itself in one way or another. This is hardly surprising, seeing that every day an elephant eats about a hundredweight and a half of vegetable matter and drinks about four hundred pints of water. Birds like storks, cranes and flamingoes sleep standing on one leg. Their knee-joints are so made that this posture costs them no active effort; on the contrary, it rests their legs. It should be realized that the standing mechanism of the more highly developed animals, including man, is based on the one hand on a complicated combined effort of the purely static structure and on the other on a series of muscle contractions which are under the continual control of the eye and the ear labyrinth. The latter constantly sends out stimuli to the whole muscle system, stimuli which keep it at an appropriate state of tension. Thus all in all static equilibrium is maintained by a triple mechanism, which makes it understandable why standing demands a considerable rise in metabolism and why it is tiring to stand for a long time. However, there are some animals—the horse, for example—for whom standing requires no activity on the part of the muscles. This explains how it is that horses are capable of standing for many hours without tiring. This position is in fact a relatively restful one for them, and they frequently sleep standing up.

As for reptiles, so far as species with transparent eyelids are concerned, such as snakes and some lizards, how or when they sleep is not clear. But tortoises, crocodiles and most lizards all shut their eyes, so that it is easy to see when they are asleep. Many creatures seek out particular spots for sleeping and form 'sleeping communities'. African cow-herons, which live on the backs of elephants, rhinoceroses and hippopotamuses collect in the evening on certain trees, to which they often have to fly quite a long way.

Burrowing animals, such as most rodents and the aardvark, build underground burrows in which to sleep. The sleeping hole proper is often furnished with soft material in order to achieve as much warmth as possible. These sleeping places are kept scrupulously clean; excrement is always deposited elsewhere.

If we compare the sleeping habits of man with those of wild mammals, a striking difference in sleeping time becomes apparent.

Insects. Above: the pill wasp Eumenes, *known for the jars which it fashions out of mud for its young (Europe, North America). Centre: Singing cicada of the genus* Cicada *from Indonesia (after Kobmann, altered). Below:* Stephanoderes, *a genus of bark beetle much feared in North America.*

(Overleaf) *Simple Insects. Above:* Tomocerus, *a typical representative of the moisture-loving ground fauna. Up to 5 millimetres long. Centre:* Orchesella, *about 4 millimetres. Below, left:* Machilis, *from 6000 feet up (Switzerland). Up to 12 millimetres long. Below, right:* Sminthurides. *Up to 1 millimetre long.*

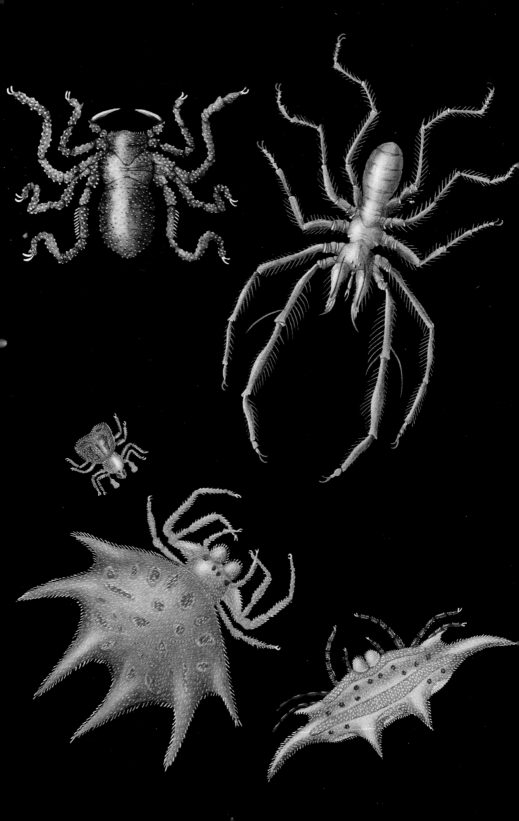

On an average, man sleeps away a third of his life, while wild animals sleep for surprisingly short periods. Adult cows and sheep hardly sleep at all, and seldom close their eyes. Chimpanzees, gorillas and orang-outangs sleep many feet above the ground in specially made nests in strong trees. In the case of the badger there are striking links between sleeping time and sunrise or sunset. When the sun sets, it leaves its burrow, almost to the minute. It disappears again into its burrow just as punctually when the sun rises. Sometimes it also takes a 'sunbath' in front of its burrow during the day.

HYGIENE

A special place in an animal's daily life is also occupied by certain hygienic habits. The cat licks its whole body with its rough tongue, while many other mammals give their coat a thorough kneading with their teeth or else comb it with their claws. The two innermost toes of a kangaroo's hind feet have become 'cleaning paws', which are quite useless for movement and serve only for cleaning the coat. Birds use their beaks to arrange and clean their feathers. A pelican's unwieldy beak does not look very suitable for this task, but a hook at the end makes cleaning work easier. The instinct to keep clean is just as highly developed in small creatures such as insects. Everyone must have noticed the house fly's ceaseless efforts to keep its body clean. Its forefeet in particular are shaped like brushes, with which head, legs and wings are polished. The larva of the European glow-worm has a kind of paint brush at the hinder end. This brush is equipped with fine little hooks, with a cleaning fluid between them. This extendible piped cleaning apparatus also serves for clinging to a surface and for moving about. In many insects the mouth is used for cleaning: the limbs are simply pushed into it. In other cases limbs have been perfected by the incorporation of a special cleaning

---

(Overleaf) *Land Bugs. Above:* Meropachys, *a South American bug whose hind legs have been transformed into powerful pincers (after Burks, modified). Centre:* Scaptocoris, *a bug that lives in Central and South America and sucks roots—an extreme example of the highly specialized miner. Below:* Diactor, *a tropical striding bug with leaf-like broadenings of the hind legs—extreme special formations, which seem to have no functional significance.*

Arachnids. Above, left: Rhizinoides, *a blind spider from equatorial Africa. Above, right:* Solifuga, *a cylindrical arachnid that lives in sand nests in Southern Russia. Its bite is feared even by men. Below:* Two Gasteracantha, *species of thorn spider from Africa. Note the great difference between the sexes: on the left the big female, on the right the dwarf male.*

mechanism, without any harmful effect to their capacity for movement. If we look at the front leg of a bee or a digging wasp, we shall find on the first joint a 'cleaning nick' filled with bristles and reminiscent of a bent comb. In addition to these built-in cleaning mechanisms, Nature has always given the creatures concerned 'instructions for use' in the form of transient reflexes and instincts.

Some animals also clean themselves by bathing. Hoofed animals in the wild state, which become covered with dust on their wanderings through desert and steppe, and with insects of every sort when they push their way through bushes and thickets, enjoy bathing in water. The wallowing of buffaloes and pigs in mud also serves for cleaning; the soft lumps of earth dry when the animals have left the pond and, after absorbing all the dirt, can easily be removed from the hide by rubbing on tree trunks or rolling on the ground. The sand-baths of hens and similar birds may also be regarded as a hygienic measure. The urge for cleanliness also extends to dwellings. The sand martins already mentioned several times carry all the droppings out of the nest with their beaks while they have young birds whose tender skin is still sensitive. If the corpse of a mouse turns up in the domain of earth-inhabiting bees and the bees cannot move it, they cover it with layers of earth, so as to isolate it as fully as possible.

Animals take great care of their progeny, and many of their efforts in this direction fall into the realm of hygiene. In the whole animal kingdom one scarcely ever sees a dirty or neglected young creature. As soon as a mammal sees the light of day it is licked thoroughly clean by its mother; this seems to be more important at first than suckling. This act of cleansing clearly awakens the maternal instinct; it is the same with a young giraffe as with a zebra foal. The small mammals—cats, rabbits, mice—behave in just the same way.

SOCIAL BEHAVIOUR

It is fascinating to trace the elements in the animal kingdom which lead to fairly close social ties. Of course, there are innumerable species which never show any signs of social behaviour, which lay eggs or produce young without worrying about what happens to them; for these animals, even pairing is only a brief meeting. Animals stream together in flocks and herds; several small groups which meet may unite, so that numbers can rise quickly. Theoretically, only members of the same species are accepted in the band, but in practice a welcome is often extended to any creature that looks more or less like the species concerned. The character of the individual is a subsidiary matter. In the North bands of lemmings grow over a period of about four years to great wandering hosts which cross rivers and often enter the sea and perish. In some years the larvae of a certain species of midge (*Sciara militaris*) form big columns up to a yard long, known in popular speech as the 'army worm' or 'snake worm' and in earlier times the basis of various superstitious stories. In the great herds of the savannah antelope, zebras and other animals all travel together; a certain physical size and long legs seem to be all that is required to gain acceptance in this mixed troop. Uniformity of action is secured by social imitation: one animal behaves just like the rest. Once a mixed throng is in movement, it sticks obstinately to the same direction; the change from one mode of behaviour can be provoked by a 'leading animal', which the rest all follow. This happens most of all when the herd is in danger and in flight. In many cases the union in a troop can be caused by over-breeding, which leads to dense population of the living space.

Besides mixed troops there are also personal communities in the animal kingdom, both in family formations and in hierarchically organized troops. In the animal kingdom, families are short-lived communities which break up when they have fulfilled their biological function—rearing the young till they are independent.

Cases of great biological interest to the sociologist are those where several creatures join forces in building a nest. African silk moth caterpillars spin bottle-shaped communal cocoons almost eighteen inches high, in which the individual cocoons for the chrysalises are then inserted. Then there are the nests of the social insects: bees, wasps, and ants. Among the mammals, the beaver builds a wonderful communal piece of work. But the social forms of the animal kingdom are unquestionably surpassed by insect colonies with their complicated social organizations. The colony-building termites, as well as many wasps, bees, and ants, have a racial history behind them in which modes of life have been modified over a period of time which is reckoned in millions of years. The basic problem of insect colonies is undoubtedly the problem of food, the intensive exploitation of the nutritional possibilities of the living space. The situation is still relatively simple in the case of bees; the numbers in each society are not so enormous and in obtaining food their ability to fly enables them to deal fairly easily with the problem of space and distance. It is different for the earth-bound ants and termites with their huge 'cities'. But they too have found ways and means of solving their food and transport problems. The nomadic species change their feeding ground as soon as the old one is exhausted. The driver ants of the warm regions are a convincing example of this. Leaf-cutter ants and many termites are 'farmers'; as we have seen, they lay out fungus gardens. Other ants are 'cattle raisers'; they keep leaf lice, bark lice, and shield lice, which they 'milk' and defend like their own young. Harvest ants construct extensive food depots, while robber ants simplify their food problem by converting to their own use the supplies of another colony. Yet other species of ants undertake raids on strange nests, steal the chrysalises and keep the workers as slaves when they hatch out. This 'breeding parasitism' is not confined to ants. There are parasitic bees, wasps, and bumble-bees, and the classic example is the cuckoo, which lays its eggs in the nests of other birds.

COMMUNICATION

No social life among animals, even on the level of the insect, is thinkable without means of communication: sounds, gestures, mimicry in all their infinite variety. Grasshoppers and crickets 'make music', ants give signals by waving their feelers, and bees have their

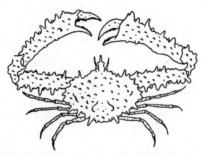

The shore crab Parthenope

dances, which serve to give news about a fresh source of food. There are all kinds of connections between animal noises on the one hand and geographical distribution, time of day and season of the year on the other. Every sound has some meaning or other. With crabs, grasshoppers and cicadas there are unmistakable links between sound and home territory. In many cases animal sounds are connected with breeding. With cicadas it is possible to distinguish the usual song, the wooing song, the female's challenge, sounds of pairing and rivalry, and cries of distress and exhaustion. Marsupials express sexual excitement with some striking noises: the opossum makes a smacking, clicking sound, the phalanger gives a braying cry, and the marsupial badger utters a curiously ringing call. Shrews use their voices a great deal during the breeding season. Other noteworthy sounds are the 'grumbling' noises of martens, polecats, wolves, foxes and so on, the barking of the arctic fox, and the howling of dingos and jackals. In the breeding season the various cats whine and howl, as we know from our domestic cat; the tiger snorts his greeting and the puma makes a miaowing noise.

Wherever the young are looked after and at least one of the parents worries about its progeny, the various noises have definite functions, especially those of the young animals. Disturbances in the state of health, especially those caused by hunger, are announced by the voice. Many parents can call their young to them by certain cries; the best-known example is provided by birds.

With mammals, sounds connected with the rearing of the young have much less significance than with birds. Smell and sight are more important. For animals that live in herds it is important that the parents should be able to recognize their young individually by their voices. Even the human ear can differentiate new-born fox cubs perfectly well by their voices. In the case of the hedgehog, the rearing of the young is done mainly by smell and sight, but even here the young animals can draw attention to themselves by making noises. A young hedgehog that has perhaps been left behind utters a twittering 'whistle of abandonment'. Little shrews cheep; they also scrape, click, and make clucking noises. Young members of the cat family make whimpering noises. Female camels and llamas utter expressive sounds just before giving birth, and the young make similar sounds, usually before and while they are suckled. Older camel foals give vent to real bellows, with their mouths wide open.

Particularly diverse sounds are found in connection with the social mode of life. One has only to think of the 'dialogues' of apes (bellowing, whispering, barking, twittering, shrieking, screaming) or of the impressive howling, audible for long distances, of members of the dog family which live together (dogs, wolves, coyotes, jackals). There are two quite different sorts of sound: the lonely howling of solitary animals and the deep, guttural howling of tightly organized packs. The little civets undertake communal expeditions in search of food, and when danger threatens they utter clear warning sounds to which their companions react. The rhythmic roaring of lions, which also hunt together, may well be the signal for the hunt to begin. Both male and female join in the roaring. It is quite conceivable that by the maintenance of the 'vocal mood' the prey are frightened out of their hiding places and fall victims more easily to their enemies. These animals' voices have a deep biological import-ance in the various phases of an animal's daily life and thus in nature as a whole.

When the physical powers, the instinct for self-preservation, and the senses of an animal decline in old age, it usually falls a victim to its enemies, even to those which it would have dealt with easily when it was younger. Big wild animals have a subtle and reliable instinct which enables them to sense whether they are confronted with an individual that can defend itself or a weak, elderly one. Sick animals hide as best they can in their lairs. Even species which do not normally live in a den seek out hiding places instinctively so as to protect themselves against their enemies. Often in illness more warmth is required or the bright light of day becomes burdensome. Even the normally footloose hare creeps into a badger's or a rabbit's burrow. The skeletons of very old baboons have been found in the most remote clefts in rock.

Creatures that fall by the wayside and die are soon destroyed by carrion-eaters of various sizes. Thanks to its powerful jaws the hyena in particular is adept at crunching up bones. The remaining hard portions—bones and the often iron-hard horns of certain hooved animals—are nibbled by rodents. The teeth of elephants and rhino-ceroses are gnawed by the hamster rat, and the larva of certain moths can tackle, with the aid of chemical substances, even the horns of the antelope and the gnu.

The notion that at the approach of death many animals go to definite 'sites for dying' is on the whole false. Plagues are often the cause of mass deaths and the remains of the corpses lying all round then form regular 'animal cemeteries'. It may occasionally happen that mortally sick creatures seek spots which offer protection from their enemies or the weather.

LIFE-SPAN

When man thinks of his own age he is often inclined to look enviously at animals which are supposed to attain a particularly great age. But not all the stories about centuries-old parrots and ancient elephants and crocodiles are true. Most land mammals do not attain a great age. Horses seldom reach 40, wild boars and red deer live to about 30, cattle to 25, dogs to 15, rats and mice about three years. With the big beasts of prey it is easy to miscalculate: lions and tigers seldom live for more than 20 years and the wolf's maximum is 15. On the other hand, elephants can live to a great age; one has been kept in captivity for 120 years. Some of the cold-blooded vertebrates are long-lived, too. The crocodile, like the toad, lives only to the age of 40, but it is known that giant tortoises can reach the age of 300 years and more. Frogs and salamanders do not live for much longer than ten years. Even among the invertebrates there are some surprising figures: a North American cicada needs 17 years to develop fully, and many queen ants live to 12 or 15. The bird spider of South America is supposed to live for ten years, and it is said that the earthworm can reach the same age. On the other hand, flies live only for one or two months; the *Ephemeridae* often no more than a day.

But even the oldest animals cannot compete with plants. The life-span of the whortleberry, which can reach the age of 40, is still fairly moderate, but the myrtle, vine and rose can all outlast 100 springs. Record ages can be read from the rings indicating a year's growth: 300 to 600 years for elms and poplars, 500 to 1000 years for oaks, 900 to 3000 for yews. Californian mammoth trees 300 feet tall and 30 feet in diameter have 4000 to 5000 rings. A thicket of blueberries in Pennsylvania, known since 1920, turned out after thorough investigations extending over a distance of more than a mile to be one single plant which had spread by underground runners from one seedling! Scientists from the American Department of Agriculture (Coville and Wherry) reckoned its age at 13,000 years—8000 years older than the pyramids.

9   *Conclusion*

The more perceptively we look around us at the varied forms of life on land and try to trace its designs and patterns, the clearer it becomes that, in spite of the variety of the phenomena and their inter-relationships, the same elementary principles are fundamentally valid: harmony and optimum, the self-regulating equilibrium of the environment and of its inhabitants. We have tried to show that the development and actions of all land organisms, however they are organized or to whichever kingdom they may belong, cannot be compared to a piece of machinery, but are conditioned on the one hand by inherited characteristics and on the other by environmental factors, according to which they vary, both individually and as a group, and by which they may be stopped, slowed down, or hastened.

Whether we are considering the environmental characteristics of lush landscapes or of hot, dry deserts; of bombsite or steppe; of masonry or rocky cliff-faces; or comparing the communities of caves and grottoes with organisms in the soil or elsewhere, we always find a balanced relationship between the members of the community and the conditions of the environment.

When beauty and perfection occur in nature, they are the living expression of inheritance and environment, of a harmonious balance dovetailing into the plan of the world as a whole.

Small Worms. Above, left: Traglochaetus, *a bristle-worm which lives in the water in subterranean cracks. (Switzerland.) Below, left:* Bunonema sp., *a threadworm from cow-dung. Other species live in moss cushions. Note the beautiful ornamentation on the surface of the body. Right:* Mesostoma, *a flatworm. Real size of these tiny worms is between 0·5 and 0·7 of a millimetre.*

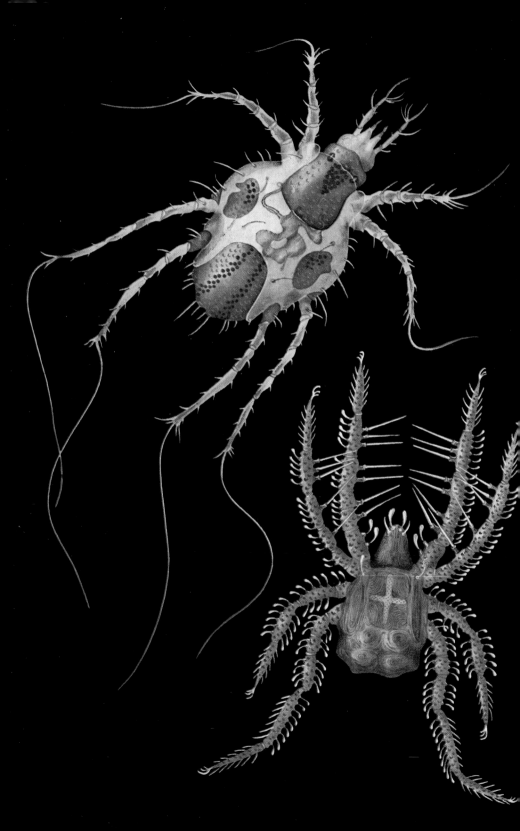

We must not forget the position of man himself in the 'eternal cycle' of life and its laws. Although modern man lives in a protected environment, created by himself, which in the course of time he has adapted more and more, he remains nevertheless a part of nature, and ecological laws are valid for him, too. Man, the 'intellectual animal', is (so far) the final link in the long chain of animal life. Like other animals, he must rely for food on what the soil gives him directly or indirectly; like them, he breathes the air around him and is subject to the laws of his environment.

Man's relationship to earth and nature is equivocal; he can be creative and protective, but also, in his egoism, blind and destructive. He can use or change, accept or destroy the landscape as he pleases. But over all stands the law of nature, governing every form of life, man not least; and man must therefore seek to play the part allotted to him in the whole complex pattern.

Mites. Above: Zwickia, *a mite that lives in the fluid of the horse-tail* Nepenthes (*Sumatra*). (*After a sketch by Thiememann.*) *Below:* Caeculus, *a curiously shaped predatory ground mite* (*Tauern, 5,600 feet.*)

N

Index

(References to illustrations are set in italics)

Volcanic soil, 145; Krakatoa, 145
Vole, 41, 54, 105, 140, *142*
Vulture, *116*

WARTHOG, 38
Wasp, 62, 134, 144, 156, 160, 180,
    181, 187
  Parasitic, 136
  Sand, 181
  Wall, 180
  Wood, 133
Water
  Animals, 77 ff., 81
  Geological activity, 11
  Plants, 68 ff.
  Pools, 137
  Shores, 89
  Springs, 88
  Vegetation, 69
Water-bear (bear animal, bear
  animalcule), 58, 65, 86, *87*, 133,
  138; eggs of, *85*
Waterbuck, 38
Water-shrew, 90
Weasel, 38, 110
Weather, 153
Weathering, biological, 13, 144
Wheat, 69

Wheel animal (rotifera), 58, *72*,
  107, 111, 133; feeding method
  of, *110*; chewing mechanism of,
  112
Whip algae, 130
Whip-scorpion, *73*
Whortleberry, 190
Wild cat, 158
Wild llama—*see* Guanaco
Willow, flying seed, 148
Wind: erosion, 12; distribution
  by, 148
Winter cyst, 64
Winter-fly, *64*
Wireworm, 59
Wolf, 66, 84, 110, 134, 139, 157,
  176, 182, 189, 191
Wombat, 46
Wood decomposition, 102, 133
Wood-louse, *149*
Wormwood, 155

YELLOW-NECKED MOUSE, eye of, *94*
Yews, 191
Young, 186, 189

ZEBRA, 84, 103, 161, 187
Zoochlorelle, 174